HOUGHTON MIFFLIN HARCOURT

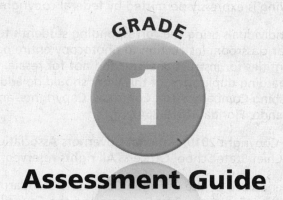

Expressions
Common Core

Dr. Karen C. Fuson

GRADE

1

Assessment Guide

This material is based upon work supported by the
National Science Foundation
under Grant Numbers
ESI-9816320, REC-9806020, and RED-935373.

Any opinions, findings, and conclusions, or recommendations expressed in this material
are those of the author and do not necessarily reflect the views of the National Science Foundation.

HOUGHTON MIFFLIN HARCOURT

GRADE 1 ASSESSMENT GUIDE

TABLE OF CONTENTS

Beginning of Year Inventory Test
Class Record Sheet

Name of Student	Counting and Cardinality	Operations and Algebraic Thinking	Number and Operations in Base Ten	Measurement and Data	Geometry

Grade 1 Beginning of Year Inventory Test Correlation

Test Item	Grade K Common Core Domain	Grade K Common Core State Standard
1	Counting and Cardinality	CC.K.CC.1
2	Counting and Cardinality	CC.K.CC.2
3	Counting and Cardinality	CC.K.CC.3
4	Counting and Cardinality	CC.K.CC.4a
5	Counting and Cardinality	CC.K.CC.5
6	Counting and Cardinality	CC.K.CC.6
7	Counting and Cardinality	CC.K.CC.7
8	Operations and Algebraic Thinking	CC.K.OA.1
9	Operations and Algebraic Thinking	CC.K.OA.1
10	Operations and Algebraic Thinking	CC.K.OA.2
11	Operations and Algebraic Thinking	CC.K.OA.3
12	Operations and Algebraic Thinking	CC.K.OA.4
13	Operations and Algebraic Thinking	CC.K.OA.5
14	Number and Operations in Base Ten	CC.K.NBT.1
15	Number and Operations in Base Ten	CC.K.NBT.1
16	Number and Operations in Base Ten	CC.K.NBT.1

Test Item	Grade K Common Core Domain	Grade K Common Core State Standard
17	Measurement and Data	CC.K.MD.1
18	Measurement and Data	CC.K.MD.2
19	Measurement and Data	CC.K.MD.3
20	Geometry	CC.K.G.1
21	Geometry	CC.K.G.2
22	Geometry	CC.K.G.3
23	Geometry	CC.K.G.4
24	Geometry	CC.K.G.5
25	Geometry	CC.K.G.6

Counting and Cardinality

Write the correct answer.

1. Write the numbers from 1 to 10.

2. Ring the numbers that are in counting order.

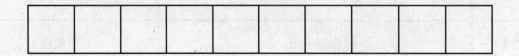

5 6 7 8 10

5 6 8 9 10

5 6 7 8 9

3. Write the missing numbers from 1 to 16.

1	2					
		11				16

4. Ring the number words that are in counting order when counting this group.

one, two, three, four, six, seven

one, two, three, four, five, six

one, two, four, three, five, six

5. How many fish are in the bowl?
Write the number.

☐ fish

---

6. Ring the group that has more.

---

7. Compare the numbers.
Circle the number that is less.

10   8

Operations and Algebraic Thinking

8. Write the partners.

$$10 = \boxed{} + \boxed{}$$

---

9. Subtract.

$$4 - 1 = \boxed{}$$

---

10. Use the drawing to help you solve.
Write the equation.

There are 5 children sitting at the table.
Then 4 more children join them.
How many children are at the table now?

_____

11. Write the partners.

7

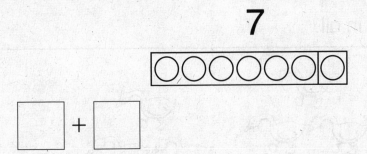

[ ] + [ ]

12. Write the missing partner.

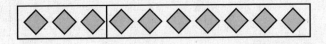

$10 = 3 +$ [ ] .

13. Subtract.

$5 - 0 =$ [ ]

Numbers and Operations in Base Ten

14. Circle ten. Write many in all.

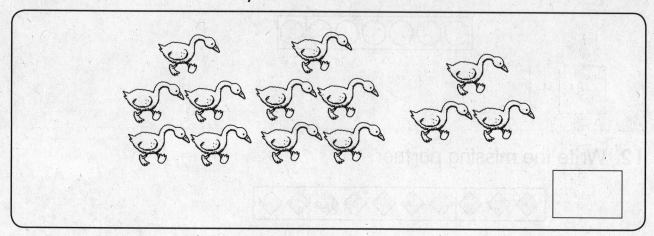

---

15. Count the ones.
Write each number.

☐ + ☐ = ☐

---

16. Complete the equation.

☐ = 10 + 6

Measurement and Data

17. Circle the word that tells how the fish could be
compared to show that they are not the same.

number   weight   color

---

18. Circle the longer object.

19. Circle every . Draw a line under every △.

Geometry

20. Circle the sphere that is next to the cone.

21. Draw a line under the rectangle.

22. Circle the shape that is **NOT** a solid.

 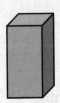

23. Circle the shape that has 6 faces.

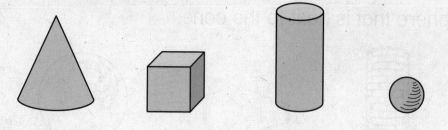

24. Cole drew this picture.

Circle the name of the shape that he
used to draw the doors on the houses.

square   triangle   rectangle

25. Join these two triangles.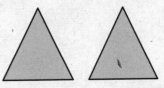

Ring the new shape they make.

  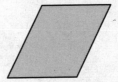

Unit _____
Class Record Sheet

Unit Objectives

Name of Student

See the 5-group.

Draw extra dots to show the number.

1.   8

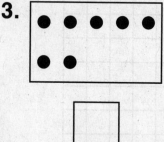

2.   10

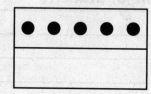

Write how many dots.

See the 5 in each group.

3.

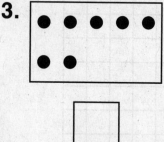

4.

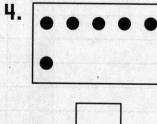

5.

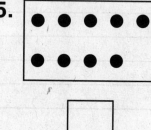

Write two more partners for the number.

1. 6 ⬜⭕⭕⭕⭕⭕⭕

$6 = 5 + 1$

$6 =$ _____

$6 =$ _____

2. 8 ⬜⭕⭕⭕⭕⭕⭕⭕⭕

$8 = 7 + 1$

$8 =$ _____

$8 =$ _____

Use doubles or patterns to solve.

3. $0 + 4 = \boxed{}$ | 4. $4 + 4 = \boxed{}$ | 5. $7 - 0 = \boxed{}$

Write the correct answer.

See the 5-group.

Draw extra dots to show the number.

1.   7

2.   8

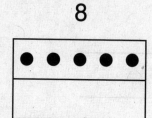

Write how many dots.

See the 5 in each group.

3.

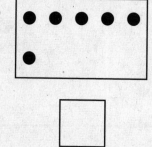

4.

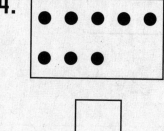

Write the 10-partners and switch the partners.

5. ●●●●●
●●●○○

_____ + _____

_____ + _____

6. ●●●●●
●○○○○

_____ + _____

_____ + _____

7. ●●●●●
○○○○○

_____ + _____

_____ + _____

8. ●●●●●
●●○○○

_____ + _____

_____ + _____

9. ●●●●●
●●●●○

_____ + _____

_____ + _____

Show the 7-partners and switch the partners.

10. ◯◯◯◯◯◯◯ [+] and [+]

11. ◯◯◯◯◯◯◯ [+] and [+]

12. ◯◯◯◯◯◯◯ [+] and [+]

Use patterns to solve.

13. $7 + 0 = \boxed{}$

14. $0 + 8 = \boxed{}$

15. $10 + 0 = \boxed{}$

16. $8 + 1 = \boxed{}$

17. $1 + 3 = \boxed{}$

18. $7 + 1 = \boxed{}$

19. $8 - 0 = \boxed{}$

20. $10 - 0 = \boxed{}$

Use patterns to solve.

21. $6 - 0 = \boxed{}$

22. $10 - 1 = \boxed{}$

23. $8 - 1 = \boxed{}$

24. $7 - 1 = \boxed{}$

25. Extended Response Draw a story about a set of 8-partners. Write the partners.

Fill in the ○ for the correct answer.

1. See the 5-group. Which drawing shows
the number 6?

○ 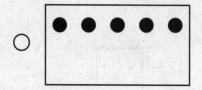   ○

○ 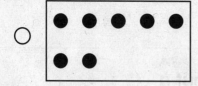   ○

---

2. See the 5-group. Which drawing shows
the number 9?

○ 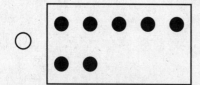   ○

○    ○

---

3. See the 5-group. What number does
the drawing show?

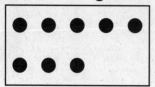

○ 8   ○ 7   ○ 6   ○ 5

4. See the 5-group. What number does the drawing show?

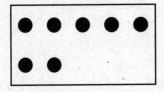

○ 4   ○ 5   ○ 6   ○ 7

What 10-partners does the drawing show?

5.

○ 4 + 6 and 6 + 4

○ 7 + 3 and 3 + 7

○ 8 + 2 and 2 + 8

○ 9 + 1 and 1 + 9

6.

○ 8 + 2 and 2 + 8

○ 7 + 3 and 3 + 7

○ 6 + 4 and 4 + 6

○ 5 + 5 and 5 + 5

7.

○ 7 + 3 and 3 + 7

○ 8 + 2 and 2 + 8

○ 9 + 1 and 1 + 9

○ 10 + 0 and 0 + 10

What 10-partners does the drawing show?

8.

○ 7 + 3 and 3 + 7

○ 8 + 2 and 2 + 8

○ 9 + 1 and 1 + 9

○ 10 + 0 and 0 + 10

9.

○ 6 + 4 and 4 + 6

○ 7 + 3 and 3 + 7

○ 8 + 2 and 2 + 8

○ 9 + 1 and 1 + 9

What 7-partners does the drawing show?

10.

○ 6 + 1 and 1 + 6

○ 3 + 4 and 4 + 3

○ 5 + 2 and 2 + 5

○ 5 + 5 and 2 + 2

What 7-partners does the drawing show?

11. ⬤⬤⬤⚪⚪⚪⚪

- ○ 5 + 2 and 2 + 5
- ○ 3 + 4 and 4 + 3
- ○ 6 + 1 and 1 + 6
- ○ 3 + 3 and 4 + 4

12. ⬤⬤⬤⬤⬤⬤⚪

- ○ 3 + 4 and 4 + 3
- ○ 5 + 2 and 2 + 5
- ○ 6 + 6 and 1 + 1
- ○ 6 + 1 and 1 + 6

Use patterns to solve.

13. $5 + 0 = $ ■

- ○ 0
- ○ 5
- ○ 6
- ○ 10

14. $0 + 9 = $ ■

- ○ 0
- ○ 8
- ○ 9
- ○ 10

15. $7 + 0 = $ ■

- ○ 6
- ○ 7
- ○ 8
- ○ 9

Use patterns to solve.

16. 6 + 1 = ▨

- ○ 7
- ○ 6
- ○ 5
- ○ 1

17. 1 + 9 = ▨

- ○ 7
- ○ 8
- ○ 9
- ○ 10

18. 5 + 1 = ▨

- ○ 4
- ○ 5
- ○ 6
- ○ 7

19. 10 − 0 = ▨

- ○ 0
- ○ 8
- ○ 9
- ○ 10

20. 7 − 0 = ▨

- ○ 6
- ○ 7
- ○ 8
- ○ 10

21. 9 − 0 = ▨

- ○ 0
- ○ 6
- ○ 8
- ○ 9

22. 9 − 1 = ▨

- ○ 8
- ○ 7
- ○ 1
- ○ 0

23. 6 − 1 = ▨

- ○ 1
- ○ 5
- ○ 6
- ○ 7

24. 10 − 1 = ▨

- ○ 0
- ○ 1
- ○ 8
- ○ 9

25. Emma drew a set of 8-partners.

Which set of 8-partners did Emma draw?

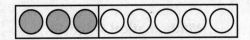

○ 1 + 7 and 7 + 1

○ 2 + 6 and 6 + 2

○ 3 + 5 and 5 + 3

○ 4 + 4 and 4 + 4

Partners and Number Patterns Through 10

What Is Assessed?

- Represent numbers 1–10.
- Find partners of numbers through 10.
- Use properties to add within 10.
- Represent addition problems.

Mathematical Practices
CC.K–12.MP.2
CC.K–12.MP.4
CC.K–12.MP.5
CC.K–12.MP.7
CC.K–12.MP.8

Materials

Crayons

Explaining the Assessment

1. Remind children that numbers 1–10 can be shown with different partners.

2. Discuss how to find partners of 7. Demonstrate how the 7-partners can be switched and the sum remains 7.

3. Read the activity aloud with the class.

Possible Responses

1. A drawing of 5 flowers in the pot. Some are red and some are yellow.

2. Children should write the partners of 5 that their drawings show; for example, $4 + 1$ and $1 + 4$.

3. A drawing of 10 flowers in the pot. Some are blue and some are yellow.

4. Children should write the partners of 10 that their drawings show; for example, $4 + 6$ and $6 + 4$.

5. Yes; Responses should indicate that there are many ways to show partners for 5 and 10.

ACTIVITY Plant Flowers

. . . .

1. Draw 5 flowers growing in the pot.
   Make some red. Make some yellow.

2. Write the 5-partners the flowers show.
   Then switch the partners.

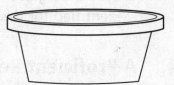

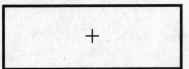 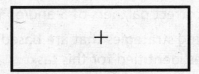

3. Draw 10 flowers growing in the pot.
   Make some blue. Make some yellow.

4. Write the 10-partners the flowers show.
   Then switch the partners.

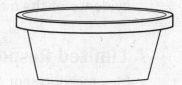

 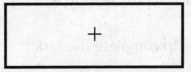

5. Could you draw other red and yellow flowers
   to show 5 and other blue and yellow flowers to
   show 10? Why or why not?

_____

_____

Performance Assessment Rubric

An Exemplary Response (4 points)

- Represents all numerals correctly
- Counts and draws groups of 5 and 10 items correctly
- Identifies and writes correct partners of 5 and 10
- Uses strategies that exemplify the mathematical practices identified for this task

A Proficient Response (3 points)

- Represents most numerals correctly
- Counts and draws groups of 5 and 10 items correctly
- Identifies and writes correct partners of 5 and/or 10
- Shows evidence of using strategies that are based in the mathematical practices identified for this task

An Acceptable Response (2 points)

- Represents some numerals correctly
- Counts and draws groups of 5 or 10 items correctly
- Identifies and writes correct partners of 5 and/or 10
- Completes the task, but approach lacks a clear strategy and evidence of the mathematical practices identified for this task

A Limited Response (1 points)

- May misrepresent many numerals
- May not correctly count or draw a group of 5 or 10 items
- Includes many errors in identifying and writing partners of 5 and 10
- Makes failed attempts to complete the task

Write the partners and the total.

1. ☐ + ☐

Total ☐

2. ☐ + ☐

Total ☐

Write the partners and total.

3. ☐ + ☐

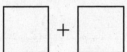

Total ☐

4. ☐ + ☐

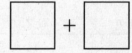

Total ☐

Write a true equation for the story.

5. 7 plates are on the table.

Anna puts 3 more plates on the table.

How many plates are on the table now?

_____

Count on to find the total.

1. $3 + 2 = \boxed{}$

2. $6 + 1 = \boxed{}$

Underline the greater number.
Count on from that number.

3. $4 + 5 = \boxed{}$

4. $6 + 3 = \boxed{}$

Draw more to count on.
Write how many in all.

5. ○○○○○

$5 + 2 = \boxed{}$

Write how many are left.

Use the picture to help you.

1. There are 7 fish.

7 − 3 = ☐

Then 3 swim away.

2. There are 10 snails.

10 − 5 = ☐

Then 5 crawl away.

Use the picture to solve the equation.

3.

7 − 5 = ☐

Subtract and write the equation.

4.

Subtract 4   _____
                              Equation

5.

Subtract 6   _____
                              Equation

Use addition to solve subtraction.

1. $5 + 3 = 8$, so I know $8 - 3 =$ ☐ .

2. $6 + 4 = 10$, so I know $10 - 4 =$ ☐ .

Solve the vertical form.
Think about addition.

3. $\begin{array}{r} 6 \\ -\ 2 \\ \hline \end{array}$
          4. $\begin{array}{r} 8 \\ -\ 1 \\ \hline \end{array}$
          5. $\begin{array}{r} 9 \\ -\ 7 \\ \hline \end{array}$

Write the correct answer.

Write the partners and the total.

1.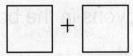

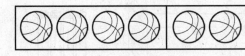

Total ☐

2.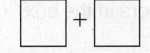

Total ☐

3.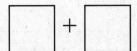

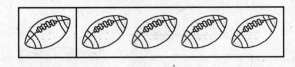

Total ☐

4.

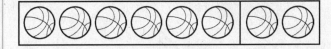

Total ☐

Write the partners and total. Then write the equation.

5.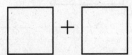

Total ☐

_____
Equation

6.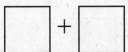

Total ☐

_____
Equation

Find the total number of toys
in the group.

7. 7 bears in the box

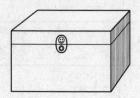

Total ☐

8. 3 crayons in the box

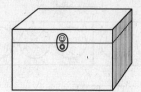

Total ☐

9. 6 robots in the box

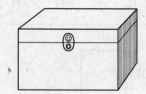

Total ☐

10. 4 blocks in the box

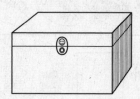

Total ☐

Underline the greater number.
Count on from that number.

11. 2 + 6 = ☐

12. 3 + 5 = ☐

13. 4 + 3 = ☐

14. 6 + 3 = ☐

15. 1 + 9 = ☐

16. 7 + 2 = ☐

Write how many are left.
Use the picture to help you.

17. There are 8 rabbits.

 $8 - 3 = \boxed{}$

Then 3 hop away.

18. There are 7 cars.

 $7 - 5 = \boxed{}$

Then 5 drive away.

Subtract and write the equation.

19. ⬤⬤⬤⬤⬤○○○○   _____

Subtract 3   Equation

20. ⬤⬤⬤⬤⬤○○○○○   _____

Subtract 6   Equation

21. ⬤⬤⬤⬤⬤○○   _____

Subtract 2   Equation

Use addition to solve subtraction.

22. $3 + 5 = 8$, so I know $8 - 5 = \boxed{}$.

23. $5 + 4 = 9$, so I know $9 - 4 = \boxed{}$.

24. $8 + 2 = 10$, so I know $10 - 2 = \boxed{}$.

---

25. Extended Response Write an equation for
the story. Make a Proof Drawing to show that
the equation is true. Write the vertical form.

> There are 7 flowers in the vase.
> Lily puts 2 more flowers in the vase.
> Now there are 9 flowers.

Name _____

Fill in the ○ for the correct answer.

Which shows the partners and the total?

1.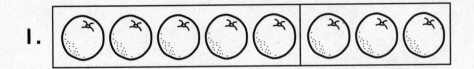

   ○ 4 + 2   Total 6
   ○ 4 + 3   Total 7
   ○ 5 + 2   Total 7
   ○ 5 + 3   Total 8

2.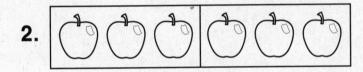

   ○ 2 + 2   Total 4
   ○ 2 + 4   Total 6
   ○ 3 + 3   Total 6
   ○ 3 + 4   Total 7

3.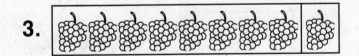

   ○ 7 + 1   Total 8
   ○ 8 + 1   Total 9
   ○ 8 + 2   Total 10
   ○ 9 + 1   Total 10

4.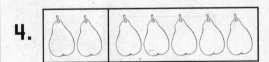

   ○ 4 + 2   Total 6
   ○ 3 + 3   Total 6
   ○ 2 + 5   Total 7
   ○ 3 + 5   Total 8

Which equation shows the partners and the total?

5.

- ○ 5 + 1 = 6
- ○ 5 + 4 = 9
- ○ 6 + 3 = 9
- ○ 6 + 4 = 10

6.

- ○ 5 + 5 = 10
- ○ 4 + 6 = 10
- ○ 4 + 5 = 9
- ○ 5 + 4 = 9

What is the total number of toys in each group?

7. 4 yo-yos in the box

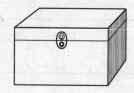

- ○ 2
- ○ 4
- ○ 6
- ○ 8

8. 7 jacks in the box

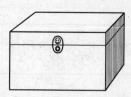

- ○ 7
- ○ 8
- ○ 9
- ○ 10

What is the total number of toys in each group?

9. 3 pinwheels in the box

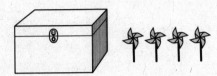

- ○ 7
- ○ 6
- ○ 4
- ○ 3

10. 5 trucks in the box

- ○ 6
- ○ 7
- ○ 8
- ○ 9

Count on to find the total.

11. $2 + 8 =$ ▨

- ○ 7
- ○ 8
- ○ 9
- ○ 10

12. $6 + 2 =$ ▨

- ○ 8
- ○ 7
- ○ 6
- ○ 4

13. $7 + 3 =$ ▨

- ○ 4
- ○ 5
- ○ 8
- ○ 10

14. $3 + 6 =$ ▨

- ○ 3
- ○ 5
- ○ 9
- ○ 10

15. $2 + 7 =$ ▨

- ○ 10
- ○ 9
- ○ 7
- ○ 5

16. $5 + 4 =$ ▨

- ○ 9
- ○ 8
- ○ 3
- ○ 1

Subtract.

17. There are 9 butterflies.

Then 2 fly away.
How many are left?

○ 4   ○ 5   ○ 7   ○ 8

18. There are 10 frogs.

Then 6 hop away.
How many are left?

○ 3   ○ 4   ○ 6   ○ 7

Which equation does the picture show?

19.

Subtract 6

○ $9 - 3 = 6$
○ $8 - 2 = 6$
○ $9 - 6 = 3$
○ $8 - 6 = 2$

Which equation does the picture show?

20. ⊘⊘⊘⊘⊘ ○○○○○

Subtract 4

- ○ $10 - 4 = 6$
- ○ $9 - 4 = 5$
- ○ $8 - 4 = 4$
- ○ $6 - 4 = 2$

21. ⊘⊘⊘⊘⊘ ○○

Subtract 2

- ○ $9 - 2 = 7$
- ○ $8 - 2 = 6$
- ○ $7 - 2 = 5$
- ○ $6 - 2 = 4$

Use addition to solve subtraction.

22. $3 + 4 = 7$, so I know $7 - 4 = $ ■ .

- ○ 8
- ○ 5
- ○ 3
- ○ 2

Use addition to solve subtraction.

23. 4 + 4 = 8, so I know 8 − 4 = ▨ .

○ 2
○ 3
○ 4
○ 5

24. 7 + 3 = 10, so I know 10 − 3 = ▨ .

○ 8
○ 7
○ 6
○ 4

25. Which true equation matches the story?

Liam has 5 toy cars.

Will gives him 4 more toy cars.

Now Liam has 9 toy cars.

○ 6 − 3 = 3
○ 9 − 4 = 5
○ 5 + 4 = 9
○ 6 + 3 = 9

Addition and Subtraction Strategies

What Is Assessed?

- Represent and solve addition and subtraction problems.
- Write and solve addition and subtraction equations.
- Use strategies to add within 10.

Mathematical Practices
CC.K–12.MP.2
CC.K–12.MP.4
CC.K–12.MP.7

Materials

Red and blue centimeter cubes (10 cubes total per child), red and blue crayons

Explaining the Assessment

1. Remind children that strategies can be used to solve addition and subtraction problems. Have children give examples of each and the corresponding strategies.

2. Read the activity aloud to the class. You may want to read one instruction at a time, and then wait for children to complete it.

Possible Responses

1. Answers will vary.

2. Answers will vary.

3. Answers will vary.

4. The equation will represent Problem 3.

5. Responses will indicate an understanding of the addition method the child used.

6. Answers will vary.

7. Responses will indicate an understanding of the subtraction method the child used.

ACTIVITY How Many?

1. Take some red cubes.

   Write the number of red cubes. _____

2. Take some blue cubes.

   Write the number of blue cubes. _____

3. Draw to show the red cubes and blue cubes.

4. Write an equation that shows
   how many cubes in all.

   ___ + ___ = ___

5. Tell how you added the cubes.

   _____

   _____

6. Write a subtraction equation.
   Make a Proof Drawing to solve it.

   ___ − ___ = ___

7. Tell how you subtracted the circles.

   _____

   _____

Performance Assessment Rubric

An Exemplary Response (4 points)

- Clearly represents addition and subtraction in pictures and equations
- Chooses and applies appropriate solution strategies
- Solves addition and subtraction correctly
- Explains clearly and accurately how each problem was solved
- Uses strategies that exemplify the mathematical practices identified for this task

A Proficient Response (3 points)

- Clearly represents addition and subtraction in pictures and equations
- Chooses and applies appropriate solution strategies
- Solves addition and subtraction correctly
- Explains how each problem was solved
- Shows evidence of using strategies that are based in the mathematical practices identified for this task

An Acceptable Response (2 points)

- Represents addition and subtraction in pictures and equations with few errors
- Chooses appropriate solution strategies but may have difficulty applying them
- Solves addition and subtraction with few errors
- May have difficulty explaining how each problem was solved
- Completes the task, but approach lacks a clear strategy and evidence of the mathematical practices identified for this task

A Limited Response (1 points)

- Represents addition and subtraction in pictures and equations with several errors
- May choose inappropriate solution strategies
- May make several errors in solutions to addition and/or subtraction
- May not explain how the addition and/or subtraction was solved
- Makes failed attempts to complete the task

Count on to find the unknown partner.

1. 2 + ⬜ = 5

2. ⬜ + 4 = 7

3. ⬜ + 5 = 9

Count on to solve.

4. 7 pencils total

How many pencils are in the box?

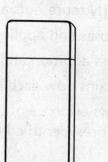

⬜ _____
   label

5. 10 pennies total

How many pennies are in the box?

⬜ _____
   label

Subtract.

1. $6 - 3 =$ ⬜ | **2.** $7 - 2 =$ ⬜ | **3.** $10 - 4 =$ ⬜

Solve the story problem.   **Show your work.**

---

4. Corey has 9 grapes.

He eats 5 of them.

How many grapes are left?

⬜ _____
    label

---

5. There are 8 kittens.

6 kittens are black.

The rest are white.

How many kittens are white?

⬜ _____
    label

Find the unknown partner or total. Watch the signs.

1. 6 − 5 = ☐ | 2. 8 + 2 = ☐ | 3. 7 − ☐ = 1

Solve the story problem.   **Show your work.**

4. Kyle catches 8 frogs.
   He lets some frogs go.
   Now Kyle has 2 frogs left.
   How many frogs did he let go?

   ☐ _____
          label

5. Some birds were in a tree. 4 birds flew away.
   Then there were 5 birds. How many birds
   were in the tree before?

   ☐ _____
          label

Name _____

Write the correct answer.

Find the unknown partner or total. Watch the signs.

1. $6 + 2 = \boxed{}$

2. $4 + 3 = \boxed{}$

3. $5 + \boxed{} = 9$

4. $3 + \boxed{} = 10$

5. $8 - 5 = \boxed{}$

6. $9 - 3 = \boxed{}$

7. $10 - \boxed{} = 6$

8. $10 - \boxed{} = 2$

Solve the story problem.   **Show your work.**

---

9. Cal has 4 blue marbles
and 4 yellow marbles.
How many marbles does he have in all?

$\boxed{}$ _____
label

---

10. There are 3 seagulls on the shore.
Then 7 more seagulls come.
How many seagulls are there in all?

$\boxed{}$ _____
label

Solve the story problem. **Show your work.**

11. Maisy has 5 red balloons.

She has some blue balloons.

Altogether she has 9 balloons.

How many blue balloons does Maisy have?

☐ _____
label

12. There are 3 ducks in the pond.

Then 5 more ducks come.

How many ducks are there now?

☐ _____
label

13. Anna sees 6 bees on a hive.

Some more bees join them.

Now there are 10 bees.

How many bees join?

☐ _____
label

14. Avery has 7 baseball cards.

Jay gives him some more baseball cards.

Now Avery has 10 baseball cards.

How many baseball cards did Jay give Avery?

☐ _____
label

Solve the story problem.

15. Lila has 10 books.

She gives 4 books away.

How many books are left?

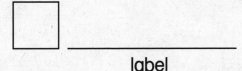

□ _____
   label

---

16. Tom picks 8 apples.

He gives some away.

Now he has 5 apples.

How many apples did Tom give away?

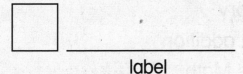

□ _____
   label

---

17. There are 9 fish. Then some
swim away. Now there are 3 fish.
How many fish swam away?

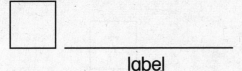

□ _____
   label

---

18. There are 10 puppies.

7 puppies are sleeping.

How many puppies are not sleeping?

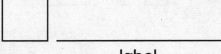

□ _____
   label

Solve the story problem.   **Show your work.**

19. Marty sees 8 birds at the feeder.
There are red birds and blue birds.
How many of each color bird could Marty see?
Show three answers.

[ ] red birds and [ ] blue birds

or [ ] red birds and [ ] blue birds

or [ ] red birds and [ ] blue birds

20. Extended Response Read the story
problem. Write a subtraction and an addition
equation for the story. Complete the Math
Mountain to match.

There are 7 leaves on the branch. 3 leaves fall
off. How many leaves are on the branch now?

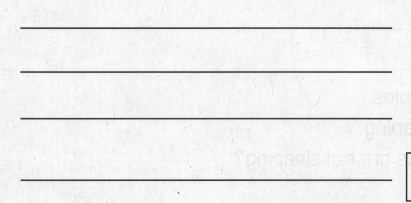

_____

_____

_____

_____

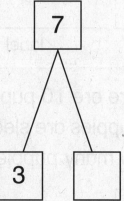

Fill in the ◯ for the correct answer.

What is the unknown partner or total? Watch the signs.

1. $5 + 3 = \blacksquare$

- ◯ 2
- ◯ 7
- ◯ 8
- ◯ 9

2. $7 + 2 = \blacksquare$

- ◯ 5
- ◯ 7
- ◯ 8
- ◯ 9

3. $6 + \blacksquare = 10$

- ◯ 4
- ◯ 5
- ◯ 6
- ◯ 16

4. $4 + \blacksquare = 9$

- ◯ 3
- ◯ 4
- ◯ 5
- ◯ 13

5. $10 - 2 = \blacksquare$

- ◯ 6
- ◯ 8
- ◯ 10
- ◯ 12

6. $8 - 4 = \blacksquare$

- ◯ 2
- ◯ 3
- ◯ 4
- ◯ 12

7. $9 - \blacksquare = 4$

- ○ 4
- ○ 5
- ○ 8
- ○ 13

8. $10 - \blacksquare = 5$

- ○ 15
- ○ 6
- ○ 5
- ○ 1

Solve the story problem.   **Show your work.**

9. Jane sees 5 horses in the field and
4 horses in the barn. How many horses
does Jane see in all?

- ○ 9
- ○ 8
- ○ 4
- ○ 1

10. 7 children are on the playground.
3 more children join them. How many
children are there in all?

- ○ 3
- ○ 4
- ○ 9
- ○ 10

Solve the story problem. **Show your work.**

11. Scott picks 8 red apples.
He picks some green apples.
Now he has 10 apples.
How many green apples does Scott pick?

○ 1
○ 2
○ 4
○ 18

12. There are 2 ants. Then 7 more ants join
them. How many ants are there now?

○ 5
○ 8
○ 9
○ 10

13. There are 4 butterflies. Some more
butterflies join them. Now there are
10 butterflies. How many butterflies join?

○ 5
○ 6
○ 12
○ 14

Solve the story problem.   **Show your work.**

14. Nina has 5 pennies. Pete gives her some
more pennies. Now Nina has 9 pennies.
How many pennies does Pete give her?

   ○ 14

   ○ 12

   ○ 9

   ○ 4

15. Mike has 8 bananas. He eats 3 of them.
How many bananas are left?

   ○ 4

   ○ 5

   ○ 10

   ○ 11

16. Megan sees 10 ladybugs. Then 2 ladybugs
fly away. How many ladybugs are left?

   ○ 8

   ○ 9

   ○ 11

   ○ 12

Solve the story problem.   **Show your work.**

17. There are 8 turtles. Then some turtles swim
away. Now there are 4 turtles. How many
turtles swim away?

○ 12

○ 10

○ 4

○ 3

18. There are 9 muffins. 6 muffins do not have
raisins. How many muffins have raisins?

○ 15

○ 12

○ 5

○ 3

Solve the story problem.   **Show your work.**

19. Megan is putting 10 leaves on a board.
She has brown leaves and gold leaves.
Which shows the number of each color
leaf Megan could have?

○ 8 brown leaves and 1 gold leaf

○ 6 brown leaves and 3 gold leaves

○ 5 brown leaves and 4 gold leaves

○ 4 brown leaves and 6 gold leaves

20. Read the story problem. Which shows
the subtraction and addition equations
for the story?

There are 9 books on a shelf.
Jose takes 6 of the books.
How many books are on the shelf now?

○ $9 - \blacksquare = 3$ and $9 + \blacksquare = 15$

○ $9 - 6 = \blacksquare$ and $6 + \blacksquare = 9$

○ $\blacksquare - 3 = 3$ and $\blacksquare + 6 = 9$

○ $\blacksquare - 3 = 6$ and $\blacksquare + 3 = 9$

Unknown Numbers in Addition and Subtraction

What Is Assessed?

- Represent and solve addition and subtraction story problems.
- Write and solve addition equations with unknowns
- Write and solve subtraction equations with unknowns.

Mathematical Practices
CC.K–12.MP.1
CC.K–12.MP.2
CC.K–12.MP.4
CC.K–12.MP.6
CC.K–12.MP.7

Explaining the Assessment

1. Have children give examples of addition and subtraction story problems. Discuss strategies to use for solving each problem. Children may suggest using drawings, Math Mountains, counting on, or equations.

2. Read the activity aloud with the class. In Problems 1 and 2, emphasize that children can choose any number at the top of the page, but that they need to choose different numbers for each problem.

Possible Responses

1–3. Answers will vary depending on which numbers children choose. Solutions may include drawings, Math Mountains, counting on, or equations.

4. Answers will vary. Sample solutions:

ACTIVITY Hide and Seek

Some children are playing hide and seek.
Choose one of these numbers for each ○.

3   4   5   7

Solve the story problems.

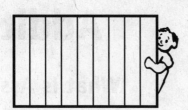

1. 10 children are playing. ○ go and hide.
   How many are left?

   ☐ _____
         label

2. ○ children are hiding. ○ more children

   hide. How many children are hiding?

   ☐ _____
         label

3. Write equations for Problems 1 and 2.

   _____   _____

4. Show you know which partners and total to write in
   each equation.

Performance Assessment Rubric

An Exemplary Response (4 points)

- Writes addition and subtraction equations and solves both correctly
- Explains clearly and accurately how each problem was solved
- Uses strategies that exemplify the mathematical practices identified for this task

A Proficient Response (3 points)

- Writes addition and subtraction equations and solves at least one correctly
- Explains how each problem was solved
- Shows evidence of using strategies that are based in the mathematical practices identified for this task

An Acceptable Response (2 points)

- May write one addition or subtraction equation incorrectly; solves at least one addition or subtraction story problem correctly
- May have difficulty explaining how each problem was solved
- Completes the task, but approach lacks a clear strategy and evidence of the mathematical practices identified for this task

A Limited Response (1 points)

- Writes incomplete addition or subtraction equations; may have difficulty solving addition and subtraction story problems
- May not explain how the addition and/or subtraction was solved
- Makes failed attempts to complete the task

Name _____

Find the total. Then make a ten.

1. $7 + 5 =$ ☐

$10 +$ ☐ $=$ ☐

2. $2 + 9 =$ ☐

$10 +$ ☐ $=$ ☐

Use doubles or doubles plus 1 to find the total.

3. $6 + 6 =$ ☐   **4.** $9 + 8 =$ ☐   **5.** $8 + 7 =$ ☐

Write the numbers.

1. | | | |

_____ tens _____ ones = _____

2. | ° °

_____ ten _____ ones = _____

Compare the numbers. Write >, <, or =.

3. 63 ◯ 73   **4.** 42 ◯ 24   **5.** 20 ◯ 20

Name _____

Add.

1. 20 + 50 = [ ]

2. 60 + 30 = [ ]

Find the total.

3. 44 + 3 = [ ]

4. 72 + 9 = [ ]

Solve the story problem.

Show your work.

5. Cindy has 56 stamps.

She buys 4 more stamps.

How many stamps does she have now?

[ ] _____
label

Name _____

Write the correct answer.

Write the numbers.

1.

_____ ten _____ ones = _____

2. ||||||

_____ tens _____ ones = _____

Draw 10-sticks and circles.

3. 32

4. 64

5. Add 1 ten.

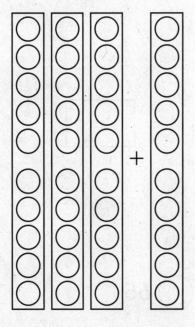

$$30 + 10 = \boxed{}$$

6. How many paper clips?

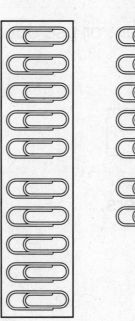

$$\boxed{}$$

How many jars are there?

7.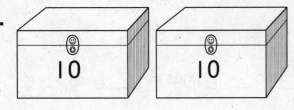

8.

Count on, make a ten, or use doubles.
Find the total.

9. $6 + 5 =$ [ ]

10. $9 + 4 =$ [ ]

Compare the numbers.
Write >, <, or =.

11. $42 \bigcirc 51$

12. $65 \bigcirc 65$

13. $87 \bigcirc 86$

14. $34 \bigcirc 14$

Solve the story problem.

15. There are 7 marbles in a jar
and 4 marbles beside the jar.
How many marbles are there?

```
┌─────────┐
│         │    _____
└─────────┘
              label
```

16. Meg has 8 red apples and
5 green apples. How many
apples does she have?

```
┌─────────┐
│         │    _____
└─────────┘
              label
```

17. There are 9 books on the
shelf. Steve adds 7 more books.
How many books are there now?

```
┌─────────┐
│         │    _____
└─────────┘
              label
```

Find the total.

18. $14 + 3 =$ ☐

19. $17 + 6 =$ ☐

20. $24 + 8 =$ ☐

21. $58 + 2 =$ ☐

Solve to complete the set of exercises.

22. $6 + 2 =$ ☐

23. $60 + 20 =$ ☐

24. $60 + 2 =$ ☐

25. Extended Response Write a number from
10 to 40. Add 1 ten. Write the new number.
Draw and write to compare the numbers.

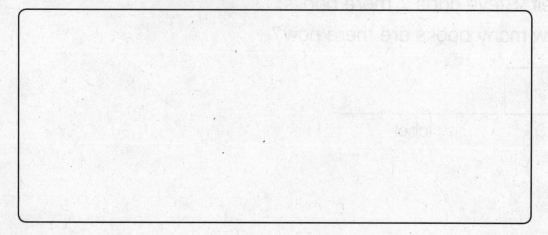

Name _____

Fill in the ○ for the correct answer.

Which does the drawing show?

1. | ○ ○ ○ ○ ○

                        ○ 1 ten 4 ones = 14
                        ○ 1 ten 5 ones = 15
                        ○ 5 tens 1 one = 51
                        ○ 5 tens 2 ones = 52

2. | | | | |

                        ○ 6 tens 0 ones = 60
                        ○ 5 tens 5 ones = 55
                        ○ 5 tens 0 ones = 50
                        ○ 0 tens 5 ones = 5

Which shows 10-sticks and circles for the number?

3. 53

4. 21

5. Which equation does the picture show?

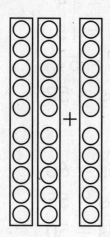

- ○ $10 + 0 = 10$
- ○ $20 + 0 = 20$
- ○ $20 + 10 = 30$
- ○ $30 + 10 = 40$

6. How many markers?

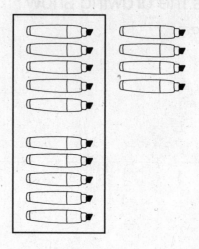

- ○ 4
- ○ 10
- ○ 14
- ○ 24

How many leaves are there?

7.

- ○ 4
- ○ 6
- ○ 10
- ○ 16

8.

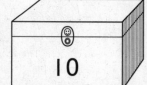 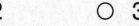 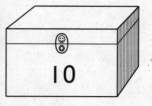

- ○ 32
- ○ 30
- ○ 23
- ○ 22

Count on, make a ten, or use doubles.

What is the total?

9. $8 + 9 = $ ▨

- ○ 16
- ○ 17
- ○ 18
- ○ 19

10. $7 + 4 = $ ▨

- ○ 3
- ○ 10
- ○ 11
- ○ 12

Which is true?

11.

- ○ $27 = 17$
- ○ $27 > 17$
- ○ $27 < 17$
- ○ $17 > 27$

12.

- ○ $80 < 79$
- ○ $79 > 80$
- ○ $79 = 80$
- ○ $80 > 79$

13.

- ○ $38 = 38$
- ○ $38 < 38$
- ○ $38 > 38$
- ○ $38 = 83$

14.

- ○ $45 > 54$
- ○ $45 < 54$
- ○ $45 = 54$
- ○ $54 < 45$

Solve the story problem.   **Show your work.**

15. Lisa has 5 animal stickers and 6 flower stickers. How many stickers does Lisa have?

- ○   1 sticker
- ○   10 stickers
- ○   11 stickers
- ○   56 stickers

16. There are 9 small plates and 8 large plates on the table. How many plates are there?

- ○   15 plates
- ○   16 plates
- ○   17 plates
- ○   18 plates

17. There are 7 birds on a tree. Then 5 more birds fly to the tree. How many birds are there now?

- ○   2 birds
- ○   12 birds
- ○   13 birds
- ○   14 birds

What is the total?

18. $19 + 1 =$

- ○ 17
- ○ 18
- ○ 19
- ○ 20

19. $17 + 4 =$

- ○ 13
- ○ 20
- ○ 21
- ○ 23

What is the total?

20. 52 + 9 = ▓

      ○ 57
      ○ 58
      ○ 60
      ○ 61

21. 69 + 3 = ▓

      ○ 66
      ○ 71
      ○ 72
      ○ 74

Solve to complete the set of exercises.

22. 5 + 4 = ▓

  ○ 10   ○ 9   ○ 8   ○ 1

23. 50 + 40 = ▓

  ○ 10   ○ 80   ○ 90   ○ 100

24. 50 + 4 = ▓

  ○ 54   ○ 50   ○ 46   ○ 44

25. Eric wrote the number 43. Then he added
1 ten. He compared the two numbers. Which
shows how Eric should compare the numbers?

○ 33 < 43
○ 43 < 44
○ 33 < 53
○ 43 < 53

Place Value Concepts

What Is Assessed?

- Read, write, and represent 2-digit numbers as tens and ones.
- Compare two 2-digit numbers.
- Use strategies to add within 20.

Mathematical Practices
CC.K–12.MP.1
CC.K–12.MP.2
CC.K–12.MP.4
CC.K–12.MP.6
CC.K–12.MP.7

Explaining the Assessment

1. Remind children how to represent 2-digit numbers with 10-sticks and circles.

2. Discuss methods for solving problems with 2-digit numbers. Emphasize efficient strategies.

3. Read the activity aloud to the class. Read one instruction at a time, and then wait for children to complete it.

Possible Responses

1. Chocolate milk; responses should indicate an understanding of place value in 2-digit number comparison.

2. Children should ring one kind of milk and show the number with 10-sticks and circles.

3. Yes; Answers will vary but should include adding 9 + 7 to find 16.

4. Children should show numbers of two or more kinds of drinks that total 20.

ACTIVITY Snack Time

It is snack time. The class has these drinks.

Milk		Juice	
Chocolate Milk	Strawberry Milk	Orange Juice	Apple Juice
13 cartons	11 cartons	9 boxes	7 boxes

1. Are there more cartons of chocolate milk or strawberry milk? How do you know?

_____

2. Ring one kind of milk. Draw 10-sticks and circles to show the number.

3. Are there enough juice boxes for 16 children? How do you know? Write or draw the answer.

4. There are 20 children in a class. Each chooses one drink. Show one way children could choose drinks.

Drink	How many?
Chocolate Milk	
Strawberry Milk	
Orange Juice	
Apple Juice	

Performance Assessment Rubric

An Exemplary Response (4 points)

- Accurately and clearly represents and compares 2-digit numbers with 10-sticks and circles

- Includes a justification that demonstrates clear understanding of addition with teen totals and an appropriate solution method

- Uses strategies that exemplify the mathematical practices identified for this task

A Proficient Response (3 points)

- Accurately and clearly represents and compares 2-digit numbers with 10-sticks and circles

- Includes a justification that demonstrates understanding of addition with teen totals and an appropriate solution method

- Shows evidence of using strategies that are based in the mathematical practices identified for this task

An Acceptable Response (2 points)

- Accurately and clearly represents 2-digit numbers with 10-sticks and circles; compares them with some knowledge of place value

- Includes a justification that demonstrates some understanding of addition with teen totals and an appropriate solution method

- Completes the task, but approach lacks a clear strategy and evidence of the mathematical practices identified for this task

A Limited Response (1 points)

- May make errors in representing 2-digit numbers with 10-sticks and circles; does not accurately compare two 2-digit numbers

- Includes a justification that demonstrates limited understanding of addition with teen totals or an appropriate solution method

- Makes failed attempts to complete the task

Name _____

Add or subtract.

1. $9 + \boxed{} = 17$ | **2.** $15 - 8 = \boxed{}$ | **3.** $7 + \boxed{} = 16$

Solve the story problem.   **Show your work.**

4. There are 14 ants. 9 ants are red and the rest
are black. How many ants are black?

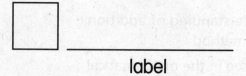

_____
label

---

5. Bailey found 4 clam shells, 5 snail shells, and
6 scallop shells. How many shells did she
find in all?

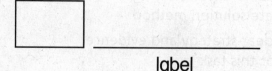

_____
label

Use the grid.

51	52	53	54	55	56	57	58	59	60
61	62	63	64	65	66	67	68	69	70
71	72	73	74	75	76	77	78	79	80

1. 10 more than 54 is ☐ .

2. 10 more than 68 is ☐ .

Add or subtract tens.

3. $68 + 30 =$ ☐

4. $52 + 20 =$ ☐

5. $80 - 50 =$ ☐

Write the correct answer.

Add.

1. $9 + \boxed{} = 15$

2. $8 + \boxed{} = 17$

3. $8 + \boxed{} = 14$

Subtract.

4. $14 - 8 = \boxed{}$

5. $16 - 7 = \boxed{}$

6. $17 - 9 = \boxed{}$

Solve the story problem.   **Show your work.**

7. 14 birds sit on a tree. Some birds fly away.
   Now there are 6 birds. How many birds
   fly away?

   $\boxed{}$ _____
              label

8. There are 15 squirrels. 6 are gray and the rest
   are brown. How many squirrels are brown?

   $\boxed{}$ _____
              label

Solve the story problem.   **Show your work.**

9. Meg had 6 stickers. Jen gave her some more stickers. Now Meg has 14 stickers. How many stickers did Jen give Meg?

☐ _____
      label

10. Beth makes 16 bracelets. She gives 8 to her friends. How many bracelets does Beth have now?

☐ _____
      label

11. Max has 7 blue marbles, 4 red marbles, and 3 green marbles. How many marbles does Max have?

☐ _____
      label

12. There are 9 red crayons, 3 green crayons, and 7 blue crayons in the box. How many crayons are in the box?

☐ _____
      label

Solve the story problem.   **Show your work.**

13. There are 12 boys and girls on the bus.
      How many boys and girls could there be?
      Show three answers.

[   ] boys and [   ] girls

or [   ] boys and [   ] girls

or [   ] boys and [   ] girls

Solve.

14. 80 + [   ] = 100

15. 40 + [   ] = 100

16. 57 + 20 = [   ]

17. 40 + 24 = [   ]

18. 80 − 40 = [   ]

19. 70 − 30 = [   ]

20. 60 − 60 = [   ]

21. 40 − 0 = [   ]

22. 70 − [   ] = 30

30 + [   ] = 70

23. 80 − [   ] = 70

70 + [   ] = 80

24. Start at 81. Count. Write the numbers through 110.

81	82	83							
91									
101									

25. Extended Response Draw 10 to 20 more triangles. Ring 10-groups. Count by tens and ones. Write the numbers.

△ △ △ △ △ △ △ △ △

△ △ △ △ △ △ △ △ △

△ △ △ △ △ △ △ △ △

△ △ △ △ △ △ △ △ △

△ △ △ △ △ △

The number of triangles is [　　　]

10 less is [　　　]. 10 more is [　　　].

Fill in the ◯ for the correct answer.

Add.

1. $7 + \blacksquare = 13$

◯ 4   ◯ 6   ◯ 8   ◯ 20

2. $7 + \blacksquare = 15$

◯ 6   ◯ 7   ◯ 8   ◯ 9

3. $9 + \blacksquare = 16$

◯ 6   ◯ 7   ◯ 8   ◯ 9

Subtract.

4. $15 - 6 = \blacksquare$

◯ 11   ◯ 9   ◯ 8   ◯ 7

5. $13 - 8 = \blacksquare$

◯ 5   ◯ 6   ◯ 11   ◯ 15

6. $16 - 8 = \blacksquare$

◯ 4   ◯ 6   ◯ 7   ◯ 8

Solve the story problem.   **Show your work.**

7. There are 14 leaves on a tree. Some
leaves fall. Now there are 8 leaves
on the tree. How many leaves fell?

○ 12   ○ 6
○ 10   ○ 4

8. There are 11 fish.
2 are blue and the rest are orange.
How many fish are orange?

○ 7   ○ 9
○ 8   ○ 11

9. Toby had 3 books.
Jim gave him some more books.
Now Toby has 11 books. How many
books did Jim give Toby?

○ 6   ○ 9
○ 8   ○ 11

10. Beth makes 16 snacks.
She gives 8 snacks to her friends.
How many snacks does Beth have now?

○ 12   ○ 9
○ 10   ○ 8

Solve the story problem. **Show your work.**

11. Jude has 8 green blocks,
4 red blocks, and 2 green blocks.
How many blocks does Jude have?

○ 12   ○ 14
○ 13   ○ 15

12. David has 6 red markers,
5 green markers, and 7 blue markers.
How many markers does David have?

○ 19   ○ 17
○ 18   ○ 16

13. There are 13 mice in the cage.
Some are brown and some are white.
Which shows the number of brown mice
and white mice that could be in the cage?

○ 9 brown and 4 white

○ 9 brown and 3 white

○ 8 brown and 4 white

○ 8 brown and 3 white

Solve.

14. $70 + \blacksquare = 80$

- ○ 40
- ○ 30
- ○ 20
- ○ 10

15. $50 + \blacksquare = 100$

- ○ 30
- ○ 40
- ○ 50
- ○ 60

16. $81 + 10 = \blacksquare$

- ○ 70
- ○ 71
- ○ 90
- ○ 91

17. $50 + 17 = \blacksquare$

- ○ 63
- ○ 67
- ○ 72
- ○ 77

18. $60 - 10 = \blacksquare$

- ○ 40
- ○ 50
- ○ 60
- ○ 70

19. $80 - 70 = \blacksquare$

- ○ 10
- ○ 20
- ○ 40
- ○ 50

Solve.

20. $90 - 90 = \blacksquare$

- ○ 0
- ○ 10
- ○ 80
- ○ 90

21. $70 - 0 = \blacksquare$

- ○ 0
- ○ 7
- ○ 10
- ○ 70

22. Which number makes both equations true?

$$90 - \blacksquare = 40$$
$$40 + \blacksquare = 90$$

- ○ 30
- ○ 40
- ○ 50
- ○ 60

23. Which number makes both equations true?

$$60 - \blacksquare = 40$$
$$40 + \blacksquare = 60$$

- ○ 20
- ○ 30
- ○ 40
- ○ 100

24. Start at 71. Count through 100.
Which number is missing?

71	72	73	74	75	76	77	78	79	80
81	82	83	84	85	86		88	89	90
91	92	93	94	95	96	97	98	99	100

○ 78   ○ 87

○ 86   ○ 97

---

25. Which number is 10 more than the
number of circles?

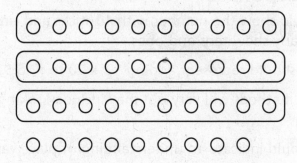

○ 39

○ 40

○ 49

○ 50

Place Value Situations

What Is Assessed?

- Add a multiple of 10 to any 2-digit number.
- Add three numbers to solve story problems.

Mathematical Practices
CC.K–12.MP.1
CC.K–12.MP.2
CC.K–12.MP.4
CC.K–12.MP.6
CC.K–12.MP.7

Explaining the Assessment

1. Remind children that they can make a drawing to show a story problem. This will help them make sense of the problem and decide whether to add or subtract.

2. Discuss how to add multiples of 10.

3. Read the task aloud with the class. You may wish to read one instruction at a time, and then wait for children to complete it.

Possible Responses

1. Children should show the number with 10-sticks and circles or other ways that clearly show tens and ones.

2. 52; drawings should represent adding 32 + 20 to find 52.

3. 14; children's methods will vary but may include looking for 10-partners to add first.

4. Responses should indicate an understanding of place value and the similarity between Problems 3 and 4.

ACTIVITY **Beach Day**

· ·

Dan and Win look for shells at the beach.

1. Dan finds 32 shells. Make a drawing to
   show 32 with tens and ones.

2. Dan finds 20 more shells. How many shells does   **Show your work.**
   he have in all?

   ☐ _____
       label

3. Win finds 8 white shells, 4 brown shells, and 2   **Show your work.**
   black shells. How many shells does she have in all?

   ☐ _____
       label

4. Win found 80 white shells, 40 brown shells, and
   20 black shells. How would you find out how many
   shells she has in all?

   _____

   _____

   _____

Performance Assessment Rubric

An Exemplary Response (4 points)

- Correctly draws tens and ones to show 32
- Adds a multiple of 10 and a 2-digit number correctly; clearly shows the operation and an appropriate solution method
- Uses at least two of the following to explain: mathematical language, symbols, and diagrams
- Demonstrates an understanding of place value in addition
- Uses strategies that exemplify the mathematical practices identified for this task

A Proficient Response (3 points)

- Correctly draws tens and ones to show 32
- Adds a multiple of 10 and a 2-digit number correctly; clearly shows at least part of the operation and solution
- Uses at least one of the following to explain: mathematical language, symbols, and diagrams
- Demonstrates an understanding of place value in addition
- Shows evidence of using strategies that are based in the mathematical practices identified for this task

An Acceptable Response (2 points)

- Draws tens and ones to show 32 with minimal errors
- Adds a multiple of 10 and a 2-digit number correctly; may not show work; may include limited mathematical reasoning
- May include limited mathematical language and reasoning
- Shows some understanding of place value in addition
- Completes the task, but approach lacks a clear strategy and evidence of the mathematical practices identified for this task

A Limited Response (1 points)

- Makes many errors in drawing tens and ones to show 32
- May add a multiple of 10 and a 2-digit number correctly; may not show work
- Does not use mathematical language and reasoning
- Does not demonstrate an understanding of place value concepts
- Makes failed attempts to complete the task

1. How many in each group?

Pencils	●	●	●	●	●	●			
Crayons	●	●	●	●	●	●	●	●	
Markers	●	●							

Use the data to complete each sentence.

2. There are ☐ more pencils than markers.

3. There are ☐ more crayons than pencils.

4. There are ☐ fewer markers than crayons.

5. There are ☐ fewer pencils than crayons.

Solve the story problem.   **Show your work.**

Complete the comparison bars.

1. Keith scores 10 points.

Eric scores 7 points. How many fewer points

does Eric score than Keith?

```
┌──────┐
│      │   _____
└──────┘       label
```

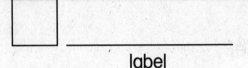

2. There are 2 more white rabbits than brown

rabbits. There are 9 brown rabbits.

How many white rabbits are there?

```
┌──────┐
│      │   _____
└──────┘       label
```

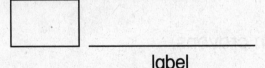

3. Don eats 6 more grapes than Meg. Meg eats

12 grapes. How many grapes does Don eat?

```
┌──────┐
│      │   _____
└──────┘       label
```

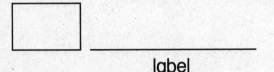

Write the correct answer.

1. Sort the animals. Record with circles.

2. Write how many in each group.

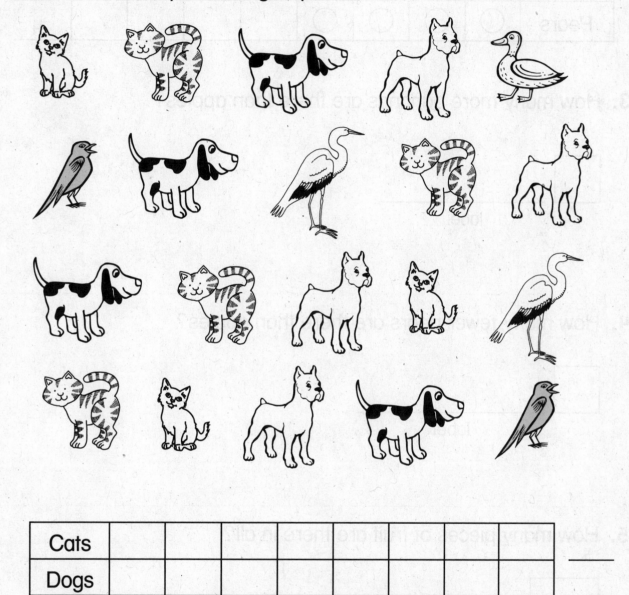

Cats								
Dogs								
Birds								

Use the data to complete.

Apples	◯	◯	◯	◯	◯	◯			6
Bananas	◯	◯	◯	◯	◯	◯	◯	◯	8
Pears	◯	◯	◯	◯					4

3. How many more bananas are there than apples?

☐ _____
　　　label

4. How many fewer pears are there than apples?

☐ _____
　　　label

5. How many pieces of fruit are there in all?

☐ _____
　　　label

Solve the story problem.   **Show your work.**
Use comparison bars.

6. Kris has 15 coins.
   Carol has 6 coins.
   How many more coins does
   Kris have than Carol?

   ☐ _____
     label

7. Rich sees 5 more cats than dogs.
   He sees 12 cats.
   How many dogs does he see?

   ☐ _____
     label

8. Joy picks 13 tulips.
   Emily picks 8 tulips.
   How many fewer tulips
   does Emily pick than Joy?

   ☐ _____
     label

Solve the story problem.
Use comparison bars.

9. Steve has 9 more pencils than markers.
He has 8 markers.
How many pencils does Steve have?

_____
label

10. Extended Response A class wants to
go on a field trip. They collect data about favorite
places to go. Each child votes. The teacher draws
one circle for each vote.

Field Trip Ideas		
Theater	Zoo	Museum
○○○ ○○	○○○○ ○○○○ ○○	○○ ○○

Write and answer two questions about the data.

_____

_____

_____

_____

Fill in the ○ for the correct answer.

1. Which table shows the correct way to sort the fruit?

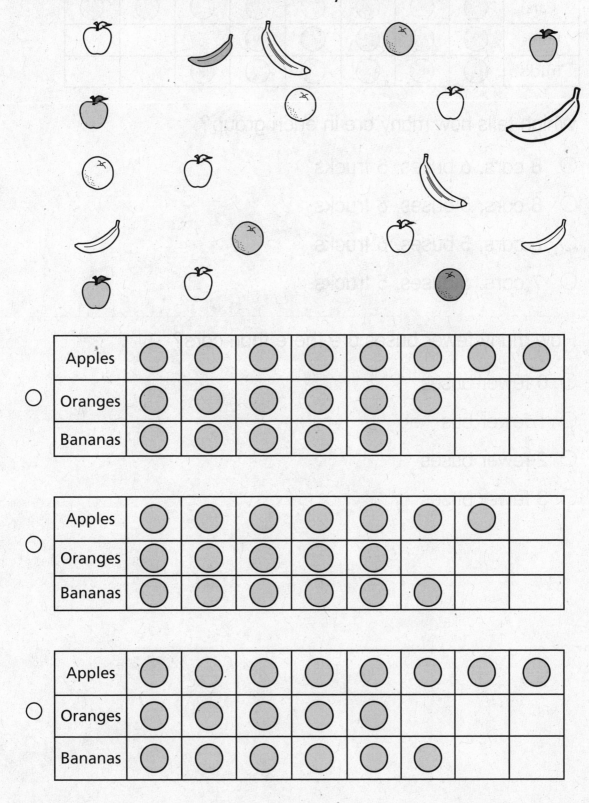

Use the data to complete.

Cars	○	○	○	○	○	○	○	○
Buses	○	○	○	○	○			
Trucks	○	○	○	○	○	○		

2. Which tells how many are in each group?

○ 8 cars, 6 buses, 5 trucks

○ 8 cars, 5 buses, 6 trucks

○ 6 cars, 5 buses, 6 trucks

○ 7 cars, 6 buses, 5 trucks

3. How many fewer buses are there than cars?

○ 0 fewer buses

○ I fewer bus

○ 2 fewer buses

○ 3 fewer buses

Use the data to complete.

Cars	◯	◯	◯	◯	◯	◯	◯	◯
Buses	◯	◯	◯	◯	◯			
Trucks	◯	◯	◯	◯	◯	◯		

4. How many more trucks are there than buses?

○ 1 more truck

○ 2 more trucks

○ 3 more trucks

○ 4 more trucks

5. How many vehicles are there in all?

○ 18 vehicles

○ 19 vehicles

○ 20 vehicles

○ 21 vehicles

Solve the story problem.
Use the comparison bars to help you.

Show your work.

6. Keegan read 8 books.
   Ann read 12 books.
   How many more books did
   Ann read than Keegan?

A	12
K	8	?

   ○ 3 more books

   ○ 4 more books

   ○ 6 more books

   ○ 20 more books

7. There are 5 more bran muffins
   than apple muffins. There are
   16 bran muffins. How many
   apple muffins are there?

B	16
A	?	5

   ○ 21 apple muffins

   ○ 18 apple muffins

   ○ 15 apple muffins

   ○ 11 apple muffins

Name _____

Solve the story problem.
Use the comparison bars to help you.

Show your work.

8. Jim counts 18 pine trees. He counts
   9 birch trees. How many fewer
   birch trees than pine trees does
   Jim count?

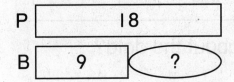

- ○ 7 fewer birch trees
- ○ 8 fewer birch trees
- ○ 9 fewer birch trees
- ○ 10 fewer birch trees

9. There are 3 more apple pies than
   peach pies. There are 8 peach pies.
   How many apple pies are there?

A	?	
P	8	3

- ○ 5 apple pies
- ○ 7 apple pies
- ○ 9 apple pies
- ○ 11 apple pies

10. Wendy's class votes for their favorite pizza.
The teacher draws one circle for each vote.

Favorite Pizza		
Cheese	Pepperoni	Veggie
○○○○ ○○○○ ○	○○○ ○○○	○○○ ○○

Which question could be answered about the data?

○ How many children like mushroom pizza?

○ How many fewer children like cheese pizza
than veggie pizza?

○ How many more children like veggie pizza
than pepperoni pizza?

○ How many children like pepperoni pizza?

Comparisons and Data

What Is Assessed?

- Organize, represent, and interpret data.
- Use addition and subtraction within 20 to solve *Compare* problems.

Mathematical Practices
CC.K–12.MP.1
CC.K–12.MP.2
CC.K–12.MP.6

Materials

Construction paper (red, blue, yellow) cut into strips; 20 for each child

Explaining the Assessment

1. Remind children that they can sort and organize information.

2. Discuss how organizing information in a table can help children solve problems.

3. Read the task aloud with the class. You may wish to read one instruction at a time, and then wait for children to complete it.

Possible Responses

1. Children should draw 5-groups and circles in the table to correctly represent the colored strips they have.

2. Answers will vary but will indicate the number of red strips.

3. Answers will vary but should indicate the number of red and yellow strips altogether.

4. Answers will vary but should indicate the difference between the color with the most strips and the color with the fewest strips.

5. Responses should indicate an understanding of the relationships among the number of red, blue, and yellow strips.

ACTIVITY Sort and Compare

Use the strips of paper for this activity.

1. Sort the strips. Draw 5-groups and circles in the table to show how many strips there are of each color.

My Color Strips		
Red	**Blue**	**Yellow**

2. How many strips are red?

☐ _____
       label

3. How many strips are **not** blue? How do you know?

_____

_____

4. How many more strips are there of the color with the most strips than the color with the fewest strips?

☐ _____
       label

5. Write 2 sentences about the data.

_____

_____

Performance Assessment Rubric

An Exemplary Response (4 points)

- Accurately draws 5-groups and circles to show data in a table for paper strips of each color
- Identifies data to compare; uses addition and subtraction to correctly solve problems
- Includes 2 well-organized sentences about the data
- Uses strategies that exemplify the mathematical practices identified for this task

A Proficient Response (3 points)

- Accurately draws 5-groups and circles to show data in a table for paper strips of each color
- Identifies data to compare; uses addition and subtraction with few or no errors to solve problems
- Includes 2 well-organized sentences about the data
- Shows evidence of using strategies that are based in the mathematical practices identified for this task

An Acceptable Response (2 points)

- Draws 5-groups and circles to show data in a table with few errors
- Identifies data to compare; uses addition and subtraction with few errors to solve problems
- Includes 2 well-organized sentences about the data
- Completes the task, but approach lacks a clear strategy and evidence of the mathematical practices identified for this task

A Limited Response (1 points)

- May draw 5-groups and circles to show data in a table with multiple errors
- Includes data to compare that may not reflect data in the table; may make a limited attempt to solve problems
- May include incomplete or inaccurate sentences about the data
- Makes failed attempts to complete the task

Read the clock.
Write the time on the digital clock.

1.

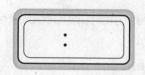

2.

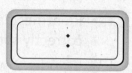

3.

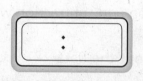

4.

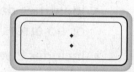

5.

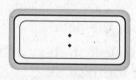

1. Draw an X on the shape that is NOT a square.

 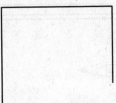

2. Ring the shapes used to make the new shape.

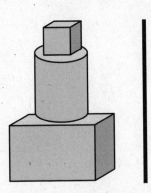   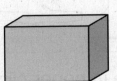

3. Draw a line to show halves.
Color one half of the shape.

4. Draw lines to show fourths.
Color one fourth of the shape.

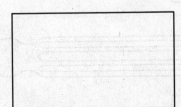

Write 1, 2, 3 in order from longest to shortest.

1. ☐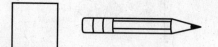

   ☐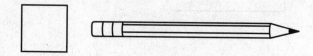

   ☐

2. ☐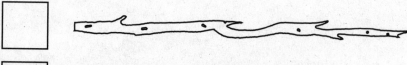

   ☐

   ☐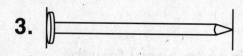

Measure in paper clips. How long?

3.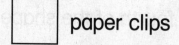

   ☐ paper clips

4.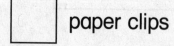

   ☐ paper clips

5.

   ☐ paper clips

Name _____

Write the correct answer.

Read the clock.

Write the time on the digital clock.

1.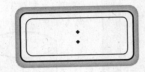

2.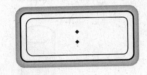

---

3. Which shapes are NOT squares?

Draw an X on each one.

  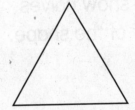

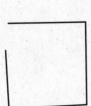 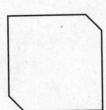  

4. Ring the shapes used to make the new shape.

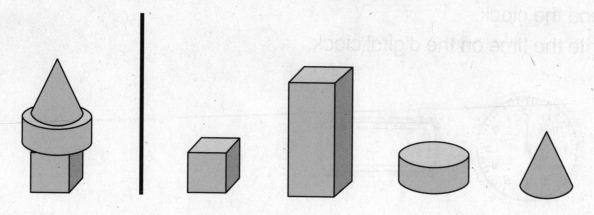

5. Ring the shape used to make the larger shape.

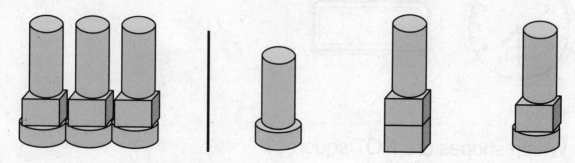

6. Draw a line to show halves.
Color one half of the shape.

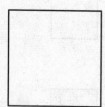

7. Draw lines to show fourths.
Color one fourth of the shape.

8. Write 1, 2, 3 in order from longest to shortest.

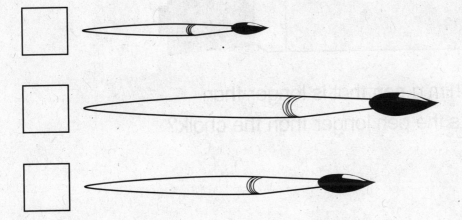

9. Measure in paper clips.

How long? ☐ paper clips

---

10. Extended Response Mason has this piece of chalk and this marker.

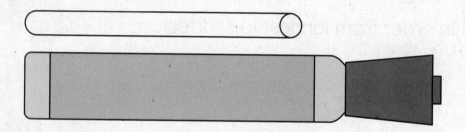

Deann gives him a pen that is longer than the marker. Is the pen longer than the chalk? Explain.

_____

_____

_____

Name _____

Fill in the ○ for the correct answer.

Read the clock.

What time does the clock show?

1.

○ 3:00   ○ 5:00

○ 4:00   ○ 6:00

2.

○ 12:30   ○ 2:30

○ 1:30   ○ 6:30

3. Which shape is NOT a triangle?

○    ○

○   ○

---

4. Which shape was NOT used to make the new shape?

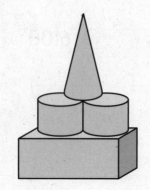

○ 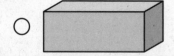   ○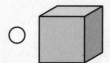

○   ○

5. Which shape was used to make the larger shape?

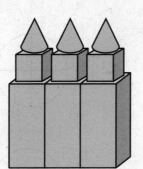

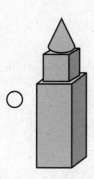   ○

○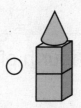

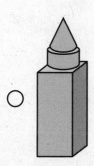   ○

○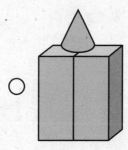

6. Which circle shows halves?

○ 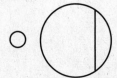   ○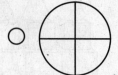

○    ○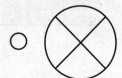

---

7. Which shows one fourth of the square shaded?

○ 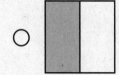   ○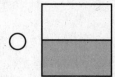

○ 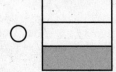   ○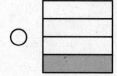

8. Which shows the strings in order from shortest to longest?

○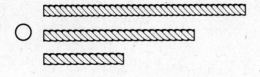

○

○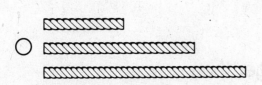

○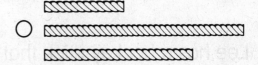

---

9. Measure in paper clips.

How long is the eraser?

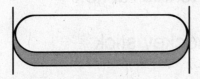

○ 1 paper clip   ○ 3 paper clips

○ 2 paper clips   ○ 4 paper clips

10. Jack has a baseball bat and a tennis racket.

Lee has a hockey stick that is longer than
Jack's baseball bat.

Which is true?

○ The hockey stick is shorter than the tennis racket.

○ The baseball bat is longer than the hockey stick.

○ The hockey stick is longer than the tennis racket.

○ The baseball bat is shorter than the tennis racket.

Geometry, Measurement, and Equal Shares

What Is Assessed?

- Tell and write time.
- Partition shapes into equal shares.
- Find the length of an object in length units.
- Order three objects by length.

Materials

paper clips, small classroom objects

Explaining the Assessment

1. This assessment requires children to apply what they learned about telling time, measuring with length units, and partitioning shapes into equal shares.

2. Discuss with children how to correctly line up units to measure objects.

3. Read the task aloud with the class. You may wish to read one instruction at a time, and then wait for children to complete it.

Possible Responses

1. Children should write the time on the clock to correctly represent 7:30.

2. Children divide the rectangle into halves horizontally, vertically, or diagonally. Some may draw a curved line.

3. The bed is approximately 2 paper clips long.

4. Drawings will vary. Each child's measurements and order should match his or her drawing and labels.

ACTIVITY Busy Bug's Bedtime

1. This is Busy Bug's bedtime.

   Write the time on the digital clock to show Busy Bug's bedtime.

2. This is Busy Bug's snack. He wants to share it with Sleepy Spider.

   Draw a line to show halves. Color half of the shape

3. This is Busy Bug's bed.

   How many paper clips long is it?

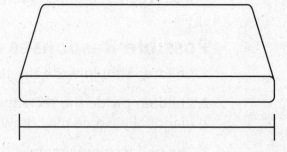

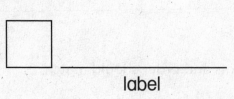

   label

4. Find objects longer and shorter than Busy Bug's bed. Draw and label a picture of all three in order by length.

Performance Assessment Rubric

An Exemplary Response (4 points)

- Tells and shows a time accurately using digital and analog clocks
- Measures length accurately in length units
- Draws a line to accurately divide a shape into halves
- Correctly orders three objects by length; clearly illustrates the order; picture is complete and labeled accurately
- Uses strategies that exemplify the mathematical practices identified for this task

A Proficient Response (3 points)

- Tells and shows times accurately using digital and analog clocks
- Measures length accurately in length units
- Draws a line to divide a shape into halves
- Orders three objects by length with minimal errors; picture is complete and labeled clearly
- Shows evidence of using strategies that are based in the mathematical practices identified for this task

An Acceptable Response (2 points)

- Tells and shows times accurately using digital and analog clocks
- Measures in length units with few errors
- Draws a line to divide a shape into halves
- Orders three objects by length with minimal errors; picture is missing no more than one element; some attempt at labeling
- Completes the task, but approach lacks a clear strategy and evidence of the mathematical practices identified for this task

A Limited Response (1 point)

- May tell or show time incorrectly using digital and analog clocks,
- May include several inaccurate measurements
- Does not accurately draw a line to divide a shape into halves
- May attempt to order three objects and include incomplete picture and/or no labels
- Makes failed attempts to complete the task

Add.

1. 27
   + 5

2. 43
   +30

3. 65
   +13

Write the vertical form. Then add.

4. 12 + 40

5. 38 + 6

Name

Write the correct answer.

Add.

1. 63
   $+29$

2. 52
   $+23$

3. 46
   $+\ 9$

4. 35
   $+20$

128

Write the vertical form. Then add.

5. 51 + 40

6. 47 + 12

7. 57 + 15

8. 82 + 6

Solve the story problem.   **Show your work.**

9. How many apples are there in all?
Show your work.

54
apples

29
apples

⬚ _____
label

10. Extended Response Write an addition
exercise that you must make a new ten to
solve. Use two 2-digit numbers. Make a
Proof Drawing.

Fill in the ○ for the correct answer.

Add.

1. 58
   + 32

   ○ 26

   ○ 80

   ○ 81

   ○ 90

2. 24
   + 15

   ○ 39

   ○ 38

   ○ 19

   ○ 11

3. 53
   + 8

   ○ 51

   ○ 55

   ○ 61

   ○ 65

4. 49
   + 30

   ○ 69

   ○ 79

   ○ 89

   ○ 99

Add.

5. 37 + 20 = ▪

   ○ 17

   ○ 39

   ○ 47

   ○ 57

6. 25 + 44 = ▪

   ○ 21

   ○ 69

   ○ 79

   ○ 96

7. 46 + 28 = ▪

   ○ 22

   ○ 64

   ○ 74

   ○ 76

8. 55 + 4 = ▪

   ○ 51

   ○ 59

   ○ 69

   ○ 95

Solve the story problem.   **Show your work.**

9. How many oranges are there in all?

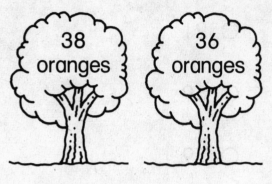

   ○ 62   ○ 72

   ○ 64   ○ 74

10. Which addition exercise must you make a new ten to solve?

   ○ 48 + 21   ○ 27 + 10

   ○ 64 + 35   ○ 16 + 19

Place Value Situations

What Is Assessed?

- Add a 2-digit and a 1-digit number.
- Add a 2-digit number and a multiple of 10.
- Add two 2-digit numbers.
- Add 2-digit numbers in a real-world context.

> **Mathematical Practices**
> CC.K–12.MP.1
> CC.K–12.MP.2
> CC.K–12.MP.4
> CC.K–12.MP.6

Explaining the Assessment

1. Remind children that they can use any workable method to add two-digit numbers.

2. Discuss how to use drawings and strategies to add.

3. Read the task aloud with the class. Let children know that you are available to help them if they have difficulty reading any instructions.

Possible Responses

1. Answers will vary but should include a method for adding a 2-digit number and a 1-digit number.

2. Answers will vary but should include a method for adding a 2-digit number and a multiple of 10.

3. Answers will vary but should include a method for adding two 2-digit numbers.

4. Answer will vary but should include a method for adding multiples of 10.

ACTIVITY **Picking Pears**
· ·

Write a 2-digit number in each ◯.
Explain how you solved the story problem.

1. Rena picks ◯ pears. Lisa   **Show your work.**
   picks 9 pears. How many pears
   do they pick in all?

   ☐ _____
        label

2. Rena and Lisa pick ◯ pears.   **Show your work.**
   Then they pick 20 more pears.
   What is the total number of pears
   they picked?

   ☐ _____
        label

3. Rena and Lisa pick ◯ pears.   **Show your work.**
   How many pears do Rena and
   Lisa pick altogether if now
   they pick ◯ more?

   ☐ _____
        label

4. If every 2-digit number in the problem ended in 0,
   would you solve it the same way? Explain.

   _____

   _____

Performance Assessment Rubric

An Exemplary Response (4 points)

- Adds a 1-digit number, a multiple of 10, or a 2-digit number to a 2-digit number correctly; clearly shows the addition, an appropriate solution method, and a thorough explanation
- Uses strategies that exemplify the mathematical practices identified for this task

A Proficient Response (3 points)

- Adds a 1-digit number, a multiple of 10, or a 2-digit number to a 2-digit number correctly; clearly shows the addition, an appropriate solution method, and an explanation
- Shows evidence of using strategies that are based in the mathematical practices identified for this task

An Acceptable Response (2 points)

- Adds a 1-digit number, a multiple of 10, or a 2-digit number to a 2-digit number correctly; shows the addition and an appropriate solution method; may not show work or explanation; may include limited mathematical reasoning
- Completes the task, but approach lacks a clear strategy and evidence of the mathematical practices identified for this task

A Limited Response (1 points)

- Makes multiple errors in adding a 1-digit number, a multiple of 10, or a 2-digit number to a 2-digit number; may include little or no explanation for answers
- Makes failed attempts to complete the task

PATH to FLUENCY **Fluency Check 1**

Add.

1. $2 + 0 =$ ☐   **2.** $0 + 4 =$ ☐   **3.** $7 + 0 =$ ☐

4. $0 + 1 =$ ☐   **5.** $3 + 0 =$ ☐   **6.** $0 + 5 =$ ☐

7. $9 + 0 =$ ☐   **8.** $0 + 8 =$ ☐   **9.** $6 + 0 =$ ☐

10. $0 + 10 =$ ☐   **11.** $5 + 0 =$ ☐   **12.** $0 + 7 =$ ☐

13. $8 + 0 =$ ☐   **14.** $0 + 9 =$ ☐   **15.** $10 + 0 =$ ☐

PATH to FLUENCY **Fluency Check 2**

Add.

1. $5 + 0 =$ ☐   **2.** $0 + 6 =$ ☐   **3.** $0 + 8 =$ ☐

4. $9 + 0 =$ ☐   **5.** $0 + 10 =$ ☐   **6.** $9 + 1 =$ ☐

7. $1 + 3 =$ ☐   **8.** $2 + 1 =$ ☐   **9.** $2 + 3 =$ ☐

10. $1 + 5 =$ ☐   **11.** $4 + 0 =$ ☐   **12.** $7 + 1 =$ ☐

13. $3 + 2 =$ ☐   **14.** $1 + 9 =$ ☐   **15.** $8 + 1 =$ ☐

PATH to FLUENCY Fluency Check 3

Subtract.

1. $1 - 0 =$ ☐

2. $3 - 1 =$ ☐

3. $2 - 0 =$ ☐

4. $4 - 1 =$ ☐

5. $6 - 0 =$ ☐

6. $5 - 1 =$ ☐

7. $7 - 0 =$ ☐

8. $8 - 1 =$ ☐

9. $9 - 1 =$ ☐

10. $8 - 0 =$ ☐

11. $9 - 0 =$ ☐

12. $7 - 1 =$ ☐

13. $10 - 0 =$ ☐

14. $6 - 1 =$ ☐

15. $10 - 1 =$ ☐

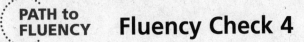

PATH to FLUENCY   **Fluency Check 4**

Subtract.

1. $1 - 1 = \boxed{}$ **2.** $2 - 0 = \boxed{}$ **3.** $2 - 1 = \boxed{}$

4. $4 - 1 = \boxed{}$ **5.** $3 - 1 = \boxed{}$ **6.** $5 - 0 = \boxed{}$

7. $3 - 2 = \boxed{}$ **8.** $5 - 1 = \boxed{}$ **9.** $6 - 0 = \boxed{}$

10. $7 - 0 = \boxed{}$ **11.** $4 - 2 = \boxed{}$ **12.** $6 - 1 = \boxed{}$

13. $8 - 1 = \boxed{}$ **14.** $9 - 0 = \boxed{}$ **15.** $5 - 2 = \boxed{}$

Add.

1. $1 + 1 =$ ☐

2. $2 + 8 =$ ☐

3. $8 + 2 =$ ☐

4. $3 + 7 =$ ☐

5. $2 + 2 =$ ☐

6. $1 + 9 =$ ☐

7. $0 + 10 =$ ☐

8. $4 + 6 =$ ☐

9. $3 + 3 =$ ☐

10. $9 + 1 =$ ☐

11. $4 + 4 =$ ☐

12. $6 + 4 =$ ☐

13. $5 + 5 =$ ☐

14. $10 + 0 =$ ☐

15. $7 + 3 =$ ☐

PATH to FLUENCY   **Fluency Check 6**

Subtract.

1. $2 - 1 =$ ☐   **2.** $4 - 3 =$ ☐   **3.** $3 - 2 =$ ☐

4. $7 - 6 =$ ☐   **5.** $6 - 5 =$ ☐   **6.** $5 - 4 =$ ☐

7. $9 - 8 =$ ☐   **8.** $8 - 7 =$ ☐   **9.** $10 - 9 =$ ☐

10. $4 - 3 =$ ☐   **11.** $6 - 5 =$ ☐   **12.** $2 - 1 =$ ☐

13. $5 - 4 =$ ☐   **14.** $10 - 9 =$ ☐   **15.** $7 - 6 =$ ☐

PATH to FLUENCY **Fluency Check 7**

Subtract.

1. $2 - 1 = \boxed{}$ 2. $3 - 3 = \boxed{}$ 3. $1 - 1 = \boxed{}$

4. $2 - 2 = \boxed{}$ 5. $4 - 2 = \boxed{}$ 6. $5 - 5 = \boxed{}$

7. $7 - 7 = \boxed{}$ 8. $6 - 6 = \boxed{}$ 9. $6 - 3 = \boxed{}$

10. $8 - 8 = \boxed{}$ 11. $8 - 4 = \boxed{}$ 12. $9 - 9 = \boxed{}$

13. $10 - 10 = \boxed{}$ 14. $10 - 5 = \boxed{}$ 15. $4 - 4 = \boxed{}$

PATH to FLUENCY

Fluency Check 8

Subtract.

1.   6
   − 2

2.   8
   − 1

3.   7
   − 0

4.   8
   − 4

5.   7
   − 3

6.   6
   − 3

7.   9
   − 4

8.   6
   − 5

9.   7
   − 2

10.   10
   − 5

11.   9
   − 6

12.   10
   − 2

13.   9
   − 7

14.   10
   − 9

15.   8
   − 5

PATH to FLUENCY Fluency Check 9

Find the unknown partner or total.

1. $3 + 3 = \boxed{}$ 2. $4 + 2 = \boxed{}$ 3. $5 + 3 = \boxed{}$

4. $3 + 4 = \boxed{}$ 5. $8 + 1 = \boxed{}$ 6. $2 + 5 = \boxed{}$

7. $4 + \boxed{} = 6$ 8. $7 + \boxed{} = 9$ 9. $1 + \boxed{} = 7$

10. $4 + \boxed{} = 8$ 11. $8 + \boxed{} = 10$

12. $3 + \boxed{} = 10$ 13. $\boxed{} + 3 = 9$

14. $\boxed{} + 5 = 8$ 15. $\boxed{} + 4 = 10$

PATH to FLUENCY **Fluency Check 10**

Find the unknown partner or total.

1. $5 + 2 = \boxed{}$ **2.** $1 + 5 = \boxed{}$ **3.** $2 + 4 = \boxed{}$

4. $5 + 4 = \boxed{}$ **5.** $2 + 6 = \boxed{}$ **6.** $5 + 5 = \boxed{}$

7. $1 + \boxed{} = 7$ **8.** $4 + \boxed{} = 6$ **9.** $0 + \boxed{} = 8$

10. $6 + \boxed{} = 9$ **11.** $2 + \boxed{} = 8$

12. $9 + \boxed{} = 10$ **13.** $\boxed{} + 3 = 6$

14. $\boxed{} + 0 = 9$ **15.** $\boxed{} + 7 = 8$

PATH to FLUENCY **Fluency Check 11**

Subtract.

1. $7 - 2 = \boxed{}$ **2.** $6 - 1 = \boxed{}$ **3.** $7 - 4 = \boxed{}$

4. $8 - 5 = \boxed{}$ **5.** $6 - 3 = \boxed{}$ **6.** $7 - 7 = \boxed{}$

7. $8 - 7 = \boxed{}$ **8.** $9 - 6 = \boxed{}$ **9.** $6 - 5 = \boxed{}$

10. $8 - 2 = \boxed{}$ **11.** $10 - 2 = \boxed{}$ **12.** $9 - 3 = \boxed{}$

13. $10 - 10 = \boxed{}$ **14.** $9 - 8 = \boxed{}$ **15.** $10 - 4 = \boxed{}$

PATH to FLUENCY   Fluency Check 12

Add.

1. $3 + 3 = \boxed{}$ **2.** $6 + 1 = \boxed{}$ **3.** $4 + 2 = \boxed{}$

4. $3 + 4 = \boxed{}$ **5.** $6 + 2 = \boxed{}$ **6.** $5 + 4 = \boxed{}$

Subtract.

7. $6 - 4 = \boxed{}$ **8.** $8 - 5 = \boxed{}$ **9.** $7 - 3 = \boxed{}$

10. $8 - 6 = \boxed{}$ **11.** $9 - 2 = \boxed{}$ **12.** $7 - 1 = \boxed{}$

13. $10 - 10 = \boxed{}$ **14.** $10 - 7 = \boxed{}$ **15.** $9 - 8 = \boxed{}$

Fluency Check 13

Add.

1. 1
  $+2$

2. 3
  $+1$

3. 2
  $+3$

4. 2
  $+4$

5. 4
  $+3$

6. 6
  $+1$

7. 4
  $+4$

8. 5
  $+2$

9. 4
  $+5$

10. 6
  $+3$

11. 5
  $+3$

12. 8
  $+2$

13. 6
  $+2$

14. 5
  $+5$

15. 2
  $+7$

Fluency Check 14

Subtract.

1. $\begin{array}{r} 4 \\ -2 \\ \hline \end{array}$

2. $\begin{array}{r} 5 \\ -1 \\ \hline \end{array}$

3. $\begin{array}{r} 3 \\ -3 \\ \hline \end{array}$

4. $\begin{array}{r} 6 \\ -5 \\ \hline \end{array}$

5. $\begin{array}{r} 7 \\ -4 \\ \hline \end{array}$

6. $\begin{array}{r} 6 \\ -3 \\ \hline \end{array}$

7. $\begin{array}{r} 8 \\ -3 \\ \hline \end{array}$

8. $\begin{array}{r} 8 \\ -8 \\ \hline \end{array}$

9. $\begin{array}{r} 7 \\ -2 \\ \hline \end{array}$

10. $\begin{array}{r} 9 \\ -6 \\ \hline \end{array}$

11. $\begin{array}{r} 8 \\ -5 \\ \hline \end{array}$

12. $\begin{array}{r} 9 \\ -4 \\ \hline \end{array}$

13. $\begin{array}{r} 10 \\ -3 \\ \hline \end{array}$

14. $\begin{array}{r} 10 \\ -8 \\ \hline \end{array}$

15. $\begin{array}{r} 9 \\ -3 \\ \hline \end{array}$

PATH to FLUENCY **Fluency Check 15**

Add.

1. $1 + 1 = \boxed{}$ **2.** $5 + 3 = \boxed{}$ **3.** $3 + 1 = \boxed{}$

4. $5 + 5 = \boxed{}$ **5.** $4 + 4 = \boxed{}$ **6.** $5 + 1 = \boxed{}$

7. $4 + 3 = \boxed{}$ **8.** $4 + 5 = \boxed{}$ **9.** $5 + 2 = \boxed{}$

Find the unknown partner.

10. $1 + \boxed{} = 8$ **11.** $3 + \boxed{} = 6$ **12.** $5 + \boxed{} = 8$

13. $\boxed{} + 3 = 9$ **14.** $\boxed{} + 5 = 10$ **15.** $\boxed{} + 2 = 10$

PATH to FLUENCY **Fluency Check 16**

Subtract.

1. $2 - 1 = \boxed{}$ **2.** $4 - 2 = \boxed{}$ **3.** $3 - 0 = \boxed{}$

4. $5 - 4 = \boxed{}$ **5.** $6 - 3 = \boxed{}$ **6.** $7 - 5 = \boxed{}$

7. $6 - 4 = \boxed{}$ **8.** $8 - 8 = \boxed{}$ **9.** $7 - 3 = \boxed{}$

10. $8 - 6 = \boxed{}$ **11.** $9 - 2 = \boxed{}$ **12.** $9 - 5 = \boxed{}$

13. $10 - 8 = \boxed{}$ **14.** $8 - 3 = \boxed{}$ **15.** $10 - 4 = \boxed{}$

PATH to FLUENCY **Fluency Check 17**

Add.

1. 0
   +1

2. 3
   +0

3. 1
   +1

4. 2
   +2

5. 1
   +5

6. 3
   +4

7. 4
   +2

8. 8
   +0

9. 2
   +5

10. 6
   +1

11. 3
   +5

12. 7
   +2

13. 2
   +8

14. 3
   +6

15. 6
   +4

PATH to FLUENCY **Fluency Check 18**

Add.

1. $2 + 2 =$ ☐   **2.** $3 + 3 =$ ☐   **3.** $1 + 3 =$ ☐

4. $3 + 2 =$ ☐   **5.** $4 + 3 =$ ☐   **6.** $1 + 7 =$ ☐

7. $2 + 4 =$ ☐   **8.** $4 + 6 =$ ☐   **9.** $6 + 2 =$ ☐

10. $7 + 2 =$ ☐   **11.** $5 + 4 =$ ☐   **12.** $7 + 3 =$ ☐

13. ☐ $= 3 + 5$ **14.** ☐ $= 2 + 8$ **15.** ☐ $= 5 + 4$

End of Year Test
Class Record Sheet

Name of Student	Operations and Algebraic Thinking	Number and Operations in Base Ten	Measurement and Data	Geometry

Grade 1 End of Year Test Correlation

Test Item	Grade 1 Common Core Domain	Grade 1 Common Core State Standard
1	Operations and Algebraic Thinking	CC.1.OA.1
2	Operations and Algebraic Thinking	CC.1.OA.2
3	Operations and Algebraic Thinking	CC.1.OA.3
4	Operations and Algebraic Thinking	CC.1.OA.5
5	Operations and Algebraic Thinking	CC.1.OA.4
6	Operations and Algebraic Thinking	CC.1.OA.6
7	Operations and Algebraic Thinking	CC.1.OA.7
8	Operations and Algebraic Thinking	CC.1.OA.8
9	Operations and Algebraic Thinking	CC.1.OA.8
10	Number and Operations in Base Ten	CC.1.NBT.1
11	Number and Operations in Base Ten	CC.1.NBT.2a
12	Number and Operations in Base Ten	CC.1.NBT.2c
13	Number and Operations in Base Ten	CC.1.NBT.2b
14	Number and Operations in Base Ten	CC.1.NBT.3
15	Number and Operations in Base Ten	CC.1.NBT.4
16	Number and Operations in Base Ten	CC.1.NBT.4

Math Expressions
© Houghton Mifflin Harcourt Publishing Company

Test Item	Grade 1 Common Core Domain	Grade 1 Common Core State Standard
17	Number and Operations in Base Ten	CC.1.NBT.5
18	Number and Operations in Base Ten	CC.1.NBT.6
19	Number and Operations in Base Ten	CC.1.NBT.6
20	Measurement and Data	CC.1.MD.1
21	Measurement and Data	CC.1.MD.2
22	Measurement and Data	CC.1.MD.3
23	Measurement and Data	CC.1.MD.3
24	Measurement and Data	CC.1.MD.4
25	Measurement and Data	CC.1.MD.4
26	Geometry	CC.1.G.1
27	Geometry	CC.1.G.1
28	Geometry	CC.1.G.2
29	Geometry	CC.1.G.2
30	Geometry	CC.1.G.3

Name _____

Operations and Algebraic Thinking

Write the correct answer.

1. Write how many are left.
Use the picture to help you.

There are 6 frogs.

 $6 - 4 =$ ☐

Then 4 hop away.

Solve the story problem.   **Show your work.**

2. Amanda has 8 flower stickers, 2 heart stickers,
and 9 car stickers. How many stickers does
Amanda have in all?

☐ _____
            label

3. Write the 10-partners
and switch the partners.

_____

_____

4. Use the 5-group.
Write how many.

☐

Solve the story problem.   **Show your work.**

5. Nina sees 9 ducks in the pond. 4 ducks are white.
   The rest are black.

   Complete the subtraction equation and the addition
   equation. How many ducks are black?

   $9 - \boxed{} = 4$

   $4 + \boxed{} = 9$

   $\boxed{}$ black ducks

6. Use addition to solve subtraction.

   $4 + 2 = 6$, so I know $6 - 2 = \boxed{}$.

7. Add both sides.
   What number makes the equation true?

   $4 + \boxed{} = 5 + 2$

8-9. Find the unknown partner.

   $6 + \boxed{} = 10$ $9 - \boxed{} = 6$

Number and Operations in Base Ten

10. Start at 61.
Write the missing numbers to 90.

61	62	63							
71									
81									

11. How many jars of paint are there?

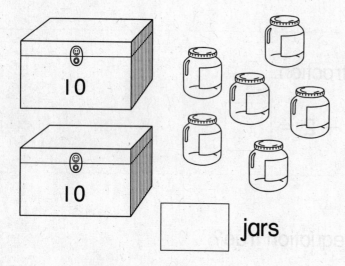

jars

12–13. Write the number.

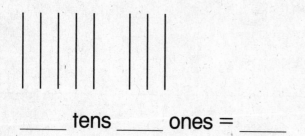

_____ tens _____ ones = _____   _____ ten _____ ones = _____

14. Compare the numbers.
Write >, <, or =.

36 ◯ 42

15–16. Add.

34
+ 7
_____

45
+ 28
_____

17. Use the grid to find 10 more.

21	22	23	24	25	26	27	28	29	30
31	32	33	34	35	36	37	38	39	40
41	42	43	44	45	46	47	48	49	50

10 more than 32 is ☐ .

18–19. Solve.

50 − 0 = ☐

60 + ☐ = 70

Measurement and Data

20. Number the cars in order from shortest to longest.

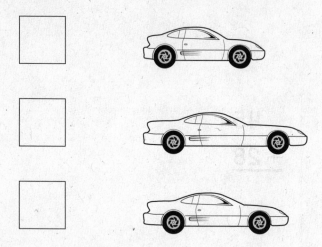

21. Count the paper clips. How long is the object?

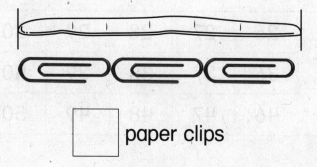

☐ paper clips

22–23. Read the clock.
Write the time on the digital clock.

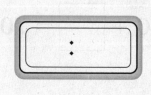

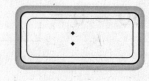

24–25. Use the data to complete.

Our Favorite Flower

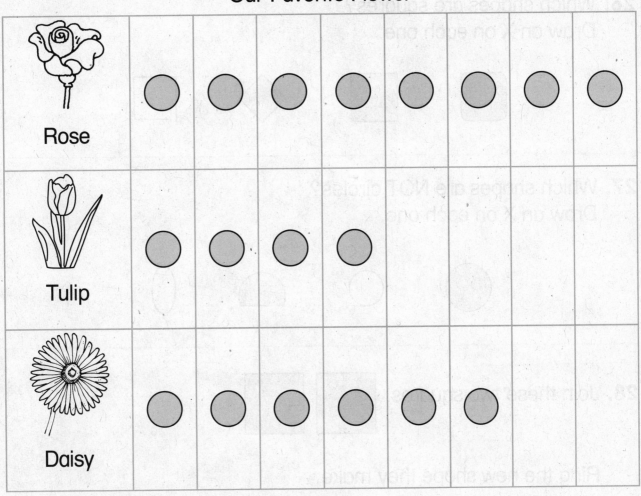

How many children chose the tulip as
their favorite flower?

☐ children

How many more children chose the
rose than the daisy?

☐ more children

Geometry

26. Which shapes are squares?
Draw an X on each one.

27. Which shapes are NOT circles?
Draw an X on each one.

28. Join these two squares.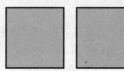

Ring the new shape they make.

End of Year Test

29. Ring the shape used to make the larger shape.

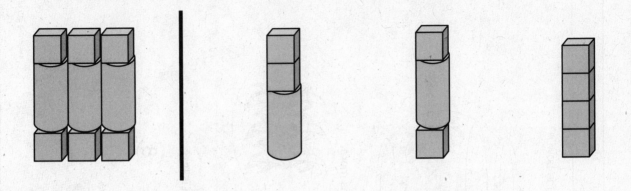

30. Draw a line to show halves.
Color one half of the shape.

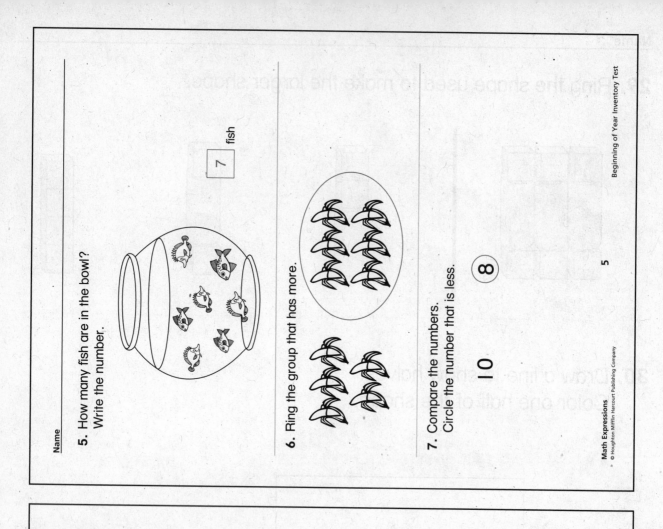

166

Name

Counting and Cardinality

Write the correct answer.

1. Write the numbers from 1 to 10.

| 1 | 2 | 3 | 4 | 5 | 6 | 7 | 8 | 9 | 10 |

2. Ring the numbers that are in counting order.

5 6 7 8 10

5 6 8 9 10

(5 6 7 8 9)

3. Write the missing numbers from 1 to 16.

| 1 | 2 | 3 | 4 | 5 | 6 | 7 | 8 |
| 9 | 10 | 11 | 12 | 13 | 14 | 15 | 16 |

4. Ring the number words that are in counting order
when counting this group.

one, two, three, four, six, seven

(one, two, three, four, five, six)

one, two, four, three, five, six

4

Name

5. How many fish are in the bowl?
Write the number.

7 fish

6. Ring the group that has more.

7. Compare the numbers.
Circle the number that is less.

10 (8)

5

Name

Operations and Algebraic Thinking

8. Write the partners.

$10 = \boxed{8} + \boxed{2}$

9. Subtract.

$4 - 1 = \boxed{3}$

10. Use the drawing to help you solve.
Write the equation.

There are 5 children sitting at the table.
Then 4 more children join them.
How many children are at the table now?

$5 + 4 = 9$

Name

11. Write the partners.

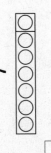

7

$\boxed{6} + \boxed{1}$

12. Write the missing partner.

$10 = 3 + \boxed{7}$

13. Subtract.

$5 - 0 = \boxed{5}$

Numbers and Operations in Base Ten

14. Circle ten. Write many in all.

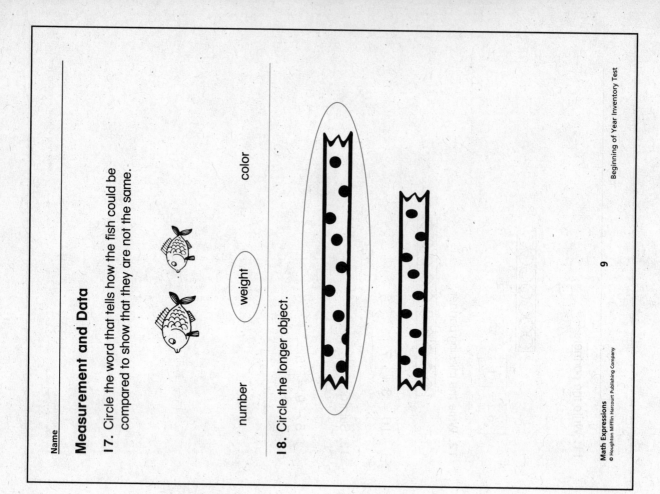

13

15. Count the ones.
Write each number.

$10 + 8 = 18$

○○○○○○○○○○   ○○○○○○○○

16. Complete the equation.

$16 = 10 + 6$

Measurement and Data

17. Circle the word that tells how the fish could be compared to show that they are not the same.

number   weight   color

18. Circle the longer object.

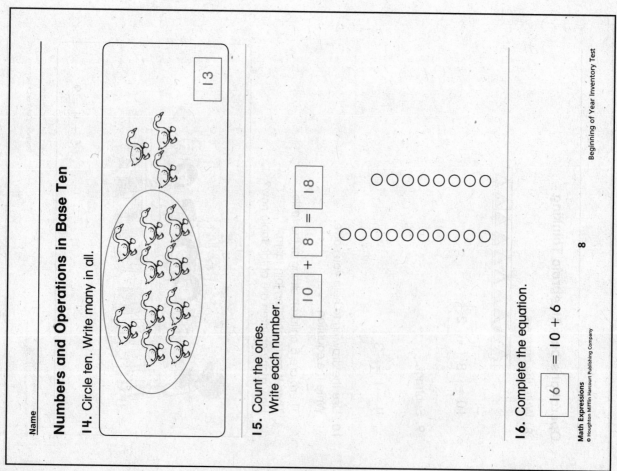

Name _____

Geometry

20. Circle the sphere that is next to the cone.

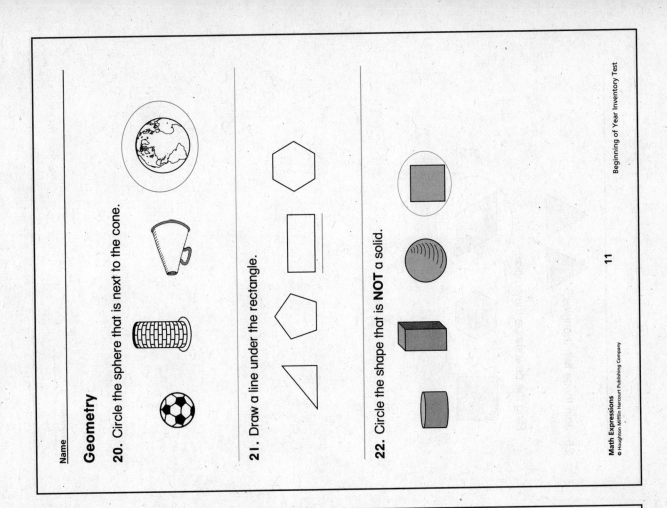

21. Draw a line under the rectangle.

22. Circle the shape that is **NOT** a solid.

Name _____

19. Circle every ▪. Draw a line under every △.

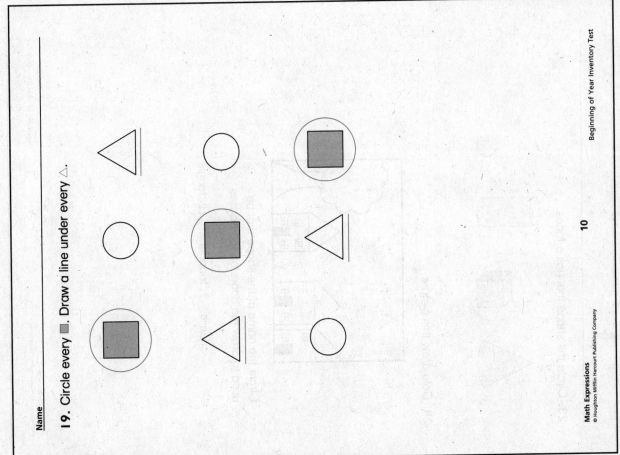

Name _____

23. Circle the shape that has 6 faces.

24. Cole drew this picture.

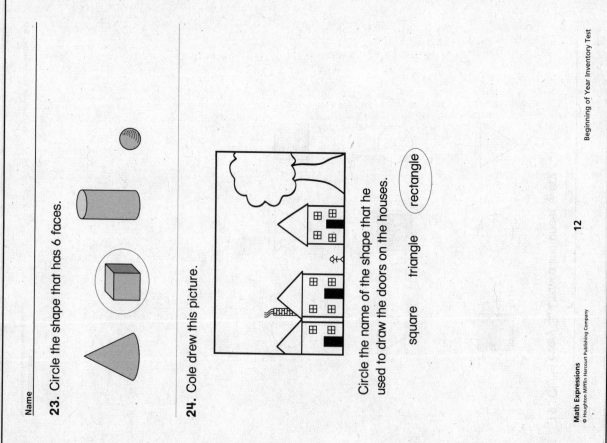

Circle the name of the shape that he
used to draw the doors on the houses.

square   triangle   (rectangle)

Name _____

25. Join these two triangles.

Ring the new shape they make.

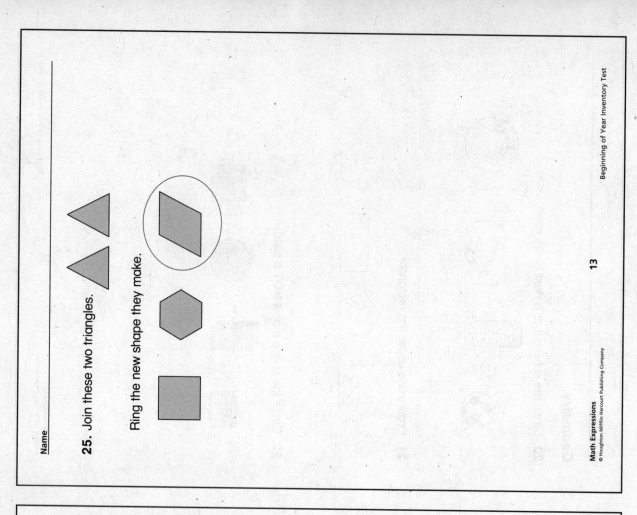

171

Unit 1 Quick Quiz 1

Name _____

See the 5-group.
Draw extra dots to show the number.

1. 8

2. 10

Write how many dots.
See the 5 in each group.

3. 7

4. 6

5. 9

Unit 1 Quick Quiz 2

Name _____

Write two more partners for the number.

1. 6

$6 = 5 + 1$

$6 = $ _____

$6 = $ _____

Possible answers: $1 + 5$;
$4 + 2$; $2 + 4$; $3 + 3$

2. 8

$8 = 7 + 1$

$8 = $ _____

$8 = $ _____

Possible answers: $1 + 7$; $6 + 2$;
$2 + 6$; $5 + 3$; $3 + 5$; $4 + 4$

Use doubles or patterns to solve.

3. $0 + 4 = \boxed{4}$ **4.** $4 + 4 = \boxed{8}$ **5.** $7 - 0 = \boxed{7}$

172

Name

Unit 1 Test Form A

Write the correct answer.

See the 5-group.
Draw extra dots to show the number.

1. 7

2. 8

Write how many dots.
See the 5 in each group.

3. 6

4. 8

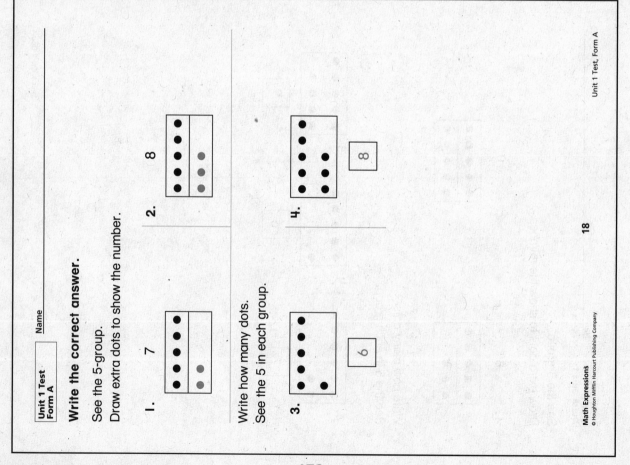

18

Name

Write the 10-partners and switch the partners.

5. $8 + 2$
   $2 + 8$

6. $6 + 4$
   $4 + 6$

7. $5 + 5$
   $5 + 5$

8. $7 + 3$
   $3 + 7$

9. $9 + 1$
   $1 + 9$

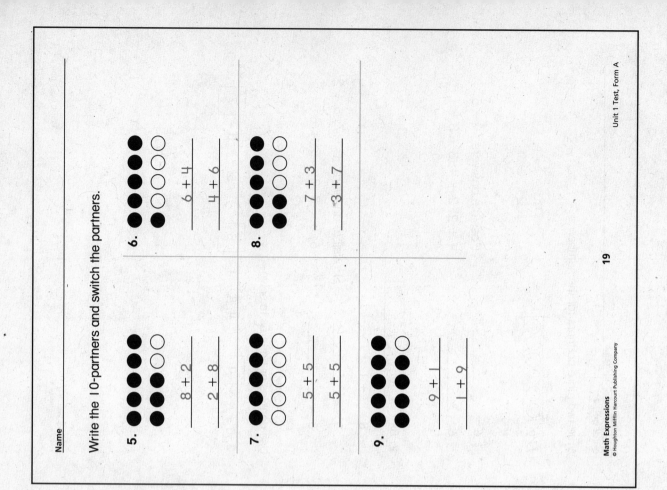

19

Use patterns to solve.

21. $6 - 0 = \boxed{6}$

22. $10 - 1 = \boxed{9}$

23. $8 - 1 = \boxed{7}$

24. $7 - 1 = \boxed{6}$

25. Extended Response Draw a story about a set of 8-partners. Write the partners.

Answers and drawings will vary.
Check children's work.

Show the 7-partners and switch the partners.

10. $1 + 6$ and $6 + 1$

11. $2 + 5$ and $5 + 2$

12. $3 + 4$ and $4 + 3$

Use patterns to solve.

13. $7 + 0 = \boxed{7}$

14. $0 + 8 = \boxed{8}$

15. $10 + 0 = \boxed{10}$

16. $8 + 1 = \boxed{9}$

17. $1 + 3 = \boxed{4}$

18. $7 + 1 = \boxed{8}$

19. $8 - 0 = \boxed{8}$

20. $10 - 0 = \boxed{10}$

Name

Fill in the ○ for the correct answer.

1. See the 5-group. Which drawing shows the number 6?

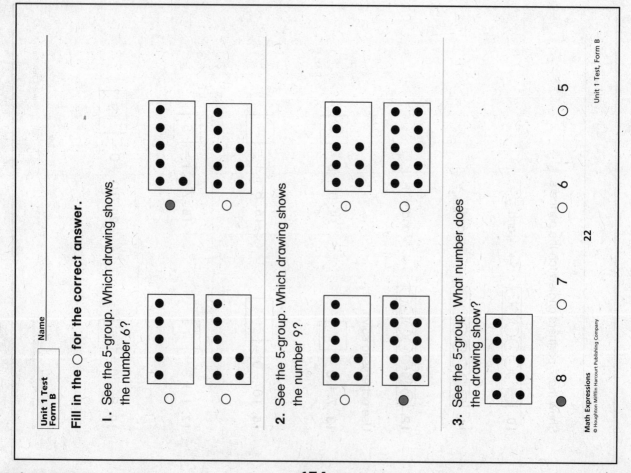

2. See the 5-group. Which drawing shows the number 9?

3. See the 5-group. What number does the drawing show?

- ● 8
- ○ 7
- ○ 6
- ○ 5

Name

4. See the 5-group. What number does the drawing show?

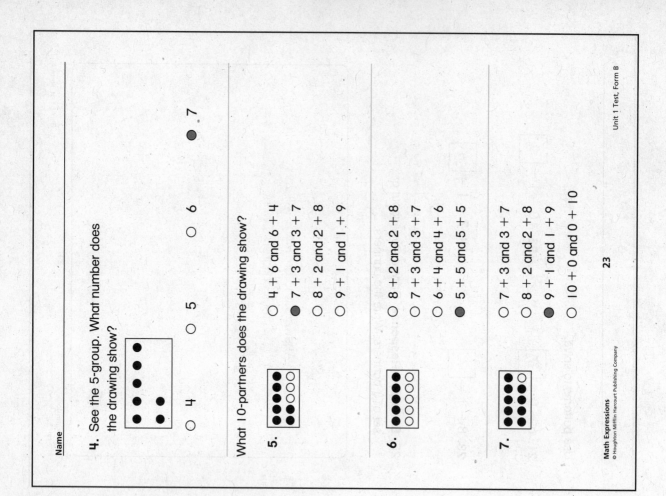

- ○ 4
- ○ 5
- ○ 6
- ● 7

What 10-partners does the drawing show?

5.
- ○ 4 + 6 and 6 + 4
- ● 7 + 3 and 3 + 7
- ○ 8 + 2 and 2 + 8
- ○ 9 + 1 and 1 + 9

6.
- ○ 8 + 2 and 2 + 8
- ○ 7 + 3 and 3 + 7
- ○ 6 + 4 and 4 + 6
- ● 5 + 5 and 5 + 5

7.
- ○ 7 + 3 and 3 + 7
- ○ 8 + 2 and 2 + 8
- ● 9 + 1 and 1 + 9
- ○ 10 + 0 and 0 + 10

What 7-partners does the drawing show?

11.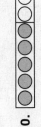

- ○ 5 + 2 and 2 + 5
- ● 3 + 4 and 4 + 3
- ○ 6 + 1 and 1 + 6
- ○ 3 + 3 and 4 + 4

12.

- ○ 3 + 4 and 4 + 3
- ○ 5 + 2 and 2 + 5
- ○ 6 + 6 and 1 + 1
- ● 6 + 1 and 1 + 6

Use patterns to solve.

13. 5 + 0 =

- ○ 0
- ● 5
- ○ 6
- ○ 10

14. 0 + 9 =

- ○ 0
- ○ 8
- ● 9
- ○ 10

15. 7 + 0 =

- ○ 6
- ● 7
- ○ 8
- ○ 9

What 10-partners does the drawing show?

8.

- ○ 7 + 3 and 3 + 7
- ● 8 + 2 and 2 + 8
- ○ 9 + 1 and 1 + 9
- ○ 10 + 0 and 0 + 10

9.

- ● 6 + 4 and 4 + 6
- ○ 7 + 3 and 3 + 7
- ○ 8 + 2 and 2 + 8
- ○ 9 + 1 and 1 + 9

What 7-partners does the drawing show?

10.

- ○ 6 + 1 and 1 + 6
- ○ 3 + 4 and 4 + 3
- ● 5 + 2 and 2 + 5
- ○ 5 + 5 and 2 + 2

25. Emma drew a set of 8-partners.
Which set of 8-partners did Emma draw?

○ 1 + 7 and 7 + 1
○ 2 + 6 and 6 + 2
● 3 + 5 and 5 + 3
○ 4 + 4 and 4 + 4

Use patterns to solve.

16. $6 + 1 =$ ▪
● 7
○ 6
○ 5
○ 1

17. $1 + 9 =$ ▪
○ 7
○ 8
○ 9
● 10

18. $5 + 1 =$ ▪
○ 4
○ 5
● 6
○ 7

19. $10 - 0 =$ ▪
○ 0
○ 8
○ 9
● 10

20. $7 - 0 =$ ▪
○ 6
● 7
○ 8
○ 10

21. $9 - 0 =$ ▪
○ 0
○ 6
○ 8
● 9

22. $9 - 1 =$ ▪
● 8
○ 7
○ 1
○ 0

23. $6 - 1 =$ ▪
○ 1
● 5
○ 6
○ 7

24. $10 - 1 =$ ▪
○ 0
○ 1
○ 8
● 9

ACTIVITY **Plant Flowers**

1. Draw 5 flowers growing in the pot.
Make some red. Make some yellow.

A drawing of 5 flowers in the pot. Some
are red and some are yellow.

2. Write the 5-partners the flowers show.
Then switch the partners. Children should write
the partners of 5 their that drawings show; for
example, 4 + 1 and 1 + 4.

| + | | + |

3. Draw 10 flowers growing in the pot.
Make some blue. Make some yellow.

A drawing of 10 flowers in the pot. Some
are blue and some are yellow.

4. Write the 10-partners the flowers show.
Then switch the partners. Children should write
the partners of 10 their that drawings show; for
example, 4 + 6 and 6 + 4.

| + | | + |

5. Could you draw other red and yellow flowers
to show 5 and other blue and yellow flowers to
show 10? Why or why not?
Yes: Responses should indicate that there are
many ways to show partners for 5 and 10.

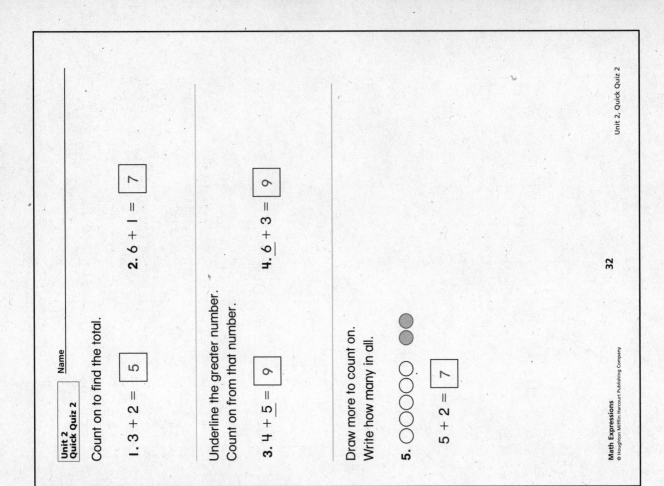

Unit 2
Quick Quiz 1 Name ______

Write the partners and the total.

1. 4 + 2

Total 6

2. 6 + 3

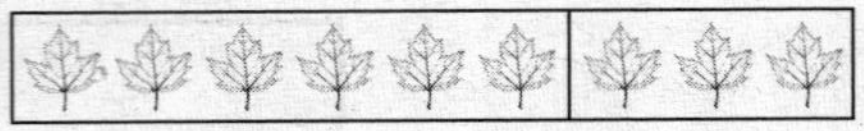

Total 9

Write the partners and total.

3. 6 + 1

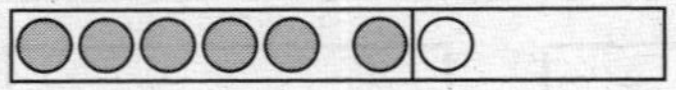

Total 7

4. 3 + 5

Total 8

Write a true equation for the story.

5. 7 plates are on the table.
Anna puts 3 more plates on the table.
How many plates are on the table now?

7 + 3 = 10

Unit 2
Quick Quiz 2 Name ______

Count on to find the total.

1. 3 + 2 = 5

2. 6 + 1 = 7

Underline the greater number.
Count on from that number.

3. 4 + <u>5</u> = 9

4. <u>6</u> + 3 = 9

Draw more to count on.
Write how many in all.

5. 

5 + 2 = 7

179

Unit 2 Quick Quiz 3

Name _____

Write how many are left.

Use the picture to help you.

1. There are 7 fish.

Then 3 swim away.

$7 - 3 = \boxed{4}$

2. There are 10 snails.

Then 5 crawl away.

$10 - 5 = \boxed{5}$

Use the picture to solve the equation.

3.

$7 - 5 = \boxed{2}$

Subtract and write the equation.

4. Subtract 4

$\underline{9 - 4 = 5}$
Equation

5. Subtract 6

$\underline{8 - 6 = 2}$
Equation

33   Unit 2, Quick Quiz 3

Unit 2 Quick Quiz 4

Name _____

Use addition to solve subtraction.

1. $5 + 3 = 8$, so I know $8 - 3 = \boxed{5}$.

2. $6 + 4 = 10$, so I know $10 - 4 = \boxed{6}$.

Solve the vertical form.
Think about addition.

3. $\begin{array}{r} 6 \\ -2 \\ \hline 4 \end{array}$

4. $\begin{array}{r} 8 \\ -1 \\ \hline 7 \end{array}$

5. $\begin{array}{r} 9 \\ -7 \\ \hline 2 \end{array}$

34   Unit 2, Quick Quiz 4

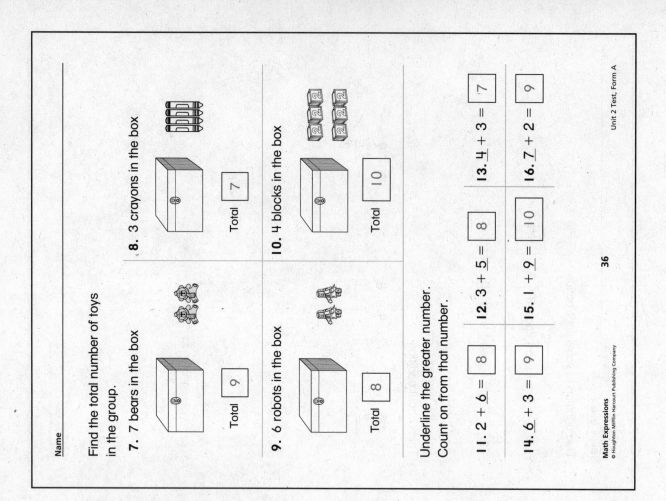

Name _____

Write the correct answer.
Write the partners and the total.

1. 4 + 3   Total 7

2. 5 + 2   Total 7

3. 1 + 4   Total 5

4. 6 + 2   Total 8

Write the partners and total. Then write the equation.

5. 3 + 2   Total 5

$$3 + 2 = 5$$
Equation

6. 5 + 4   Total 9

$$5 + 4 = 9$$
Equation

Find the total number of toys in the group.

7. 7 bears in the box   Total 9

8. 3 crayons in the box   Total 7

9. 6 robots in the box   Total 8

10. 4 blocks in the box   Total 10

Underline the greater number.
Count on from that number.

11. 2 + <u>6</u> = 8

12. 3 + <u>5</u> = 8

13. <u>4</u> + 3 = 7

14. <u>6</u> + 3 = 9

15. 1 + <u>9</u> = 10

16. <u>7</u> + 2 = 9

Name _____

Write how many are left.
Use the picture to help you.

17. There are 8 rabbits.
[rabbits] Then 3 hop away.

$8 - 3 = \boxed{5}$

18. There are 7 cars.
[cars] Then 5 drive away.

$7 - 5 = \boxed{2}$

Subtract and write the equation.

19.

$9 - 3 = 6$

Subtract 3 | Equation

20. [circles]

$10 - 6 = 4$

Subtract 6 | Equation

21. [circles]

$7 - 2 = 5$

Subtract 2 | Equation

Name _____

Use addition to solve subtraction.

22. $3 + 5 = 8$, so I know $8 - 5 = \boxed{3}$.

23. $5 + 4 = 9$, so I know $9 - 4 = \boxed{5}$.

24. $8 + 2 = 10$, so I know $10 - 2 = \boxed{8}$.

25. **Extended Response** Write an equation for the story. Make a Proof Drawing to show that the equation is true. Write the vertical form.

There are 7 flowers in the vase.
Lily puts 2 more flowers in the vase.
Now there are 9 flowers.

Possible drawing is given.

[circles]

$7 + 2 = 9$

$$\begin{array}{r} 7 \\ +2 \\ \hline 9 \end{array}$$

Name

Fill in the ○ for the correct answer.

Which shows the partners and the total?

1.
   - ○ 4 + 2   Total 6
   - ○ 4 + 3   Total 7
   - ○ 5 + 2   Total 7
   - ● 5 + 3   Total 8

2.
   - ○ 2 + 2   Total 4
   - ○ 2 + 4   Total 6
   - ● 3 + 3   Total 6
   - ○ 3 + 4   Total 7

3.
   - ○ 7 + 1   Total 8
   - ● 8 + 1   Total 9
   - ○ 8 + 2   Total 10
   - ○ 9 + 1   Total 10

4.
   - ○ 4 + 2   Total 6
   - ○ 3 + 3   Total 6
   - ● 2 + 5   Total 7
   - ○ 3 + 5   Total 8

Name

Which equation shows the partners and the total?

5.
   - ○ 5 + 1 = 6
   - ○ 5 + 4 = 9
   - ● 6 + 3 = 9
   - ○ 6 + 4 = 10

6.
   - ● 5 + 5 = 10
   - ○ 4 + 6 = 10
   - ○ 4 + 5 = 9
   - ○ 5 + 4 = 9

What is the total number of toys in each group?

7. 4 yo-yos in the box
   - ○ 2
   - ○ 4
   - ● 6
   - ○ 8

8. 7 jacks in the box
   - ○ 7
   - ○ 8
   - ○ 9
   - ● 10

Subtract.

17. There are 9 butterflies.

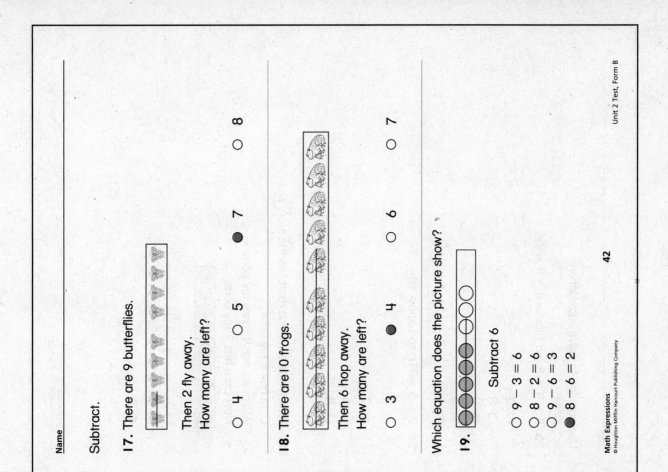

Then 2 fly away.
How many are left?

○ 4   ○ 5   ● 7   ○ 8

18. There are 10 frogs.

Then 6 hop away.
How many are left?

○ 3   ● 4   ○ 6   ○ 7

19. Which equation does the picture show?

Subtract 6

○ 9 − 3 = 6
○ 8 − 2 = 6
○ 9 − 6 = 3
● 8 − 6 = 2

Math Expressions
© Houghton Mifflin Harcourt Publishing Company

What is the total number of toys in each group?

9. 3 pinwheels in the box

● 7
○ 6
○ 4
○ 3

10. 5 trucks in the box

○ 6
● 7
○ 8
○ 9

Count on to find the total.

11. 2 + 8 =

○ 7
○ 8
○ 9
● 10

12. 6 + 2 =

● 8
○ 7
○ 6
○ 4

13. 7 + 3 =

○ 4
○ 5
○ 8
● 10

14. 3 + 6 =

○ 3
○ 5
● 9
○ 10

15. 2 + 7 =

○ 10
● 9
○ 7
○ 5

16. 5 + 4 =

● 9
○ 8
○ 3
○ 1

Math Expressions
© Houghton Mifflin Harcourt Publishing Company

Use addition to solve subtraction.

23. $4 + 4 = 8$, so I know $8 - 4 = \blacksquare$.
- ○ 2
- ○ 3
- ● 4
- ○ 5

24. $7 + 3 = 10$, so I know $10 - 3 = \blacksquare$.
- ○ 8
- ● 7
- ○ 6
- ○ 4

25. Which true equation matches the story?

Liam has 5 toy cars.
Will gives him 4 more toy cars.
Now Liam has 9 toy cars.

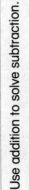

- ○ $6 - 3 = 3$
- ○ $9 - 4 = 5$
- ● $5 + 4 = 9$
- ○ $6 + 3 = 9$

Which equation does the picture show?

20.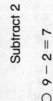

Subtract 4
- ● $10 - 4 = 6$
- ○ $9 - 4 = 5$
- ○ $8 - 4 = 4$
- ○ $6 - 4 = 2$

21.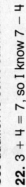

Subtract 2
- ○ $9 - 2 = 7$
- ○ $8 - 2 = 6$
- ● $7 - 2 = 5$
- ○ $6 - 2 = 4$

Use addition to solve subtraction.

22. $3 + 4 = 7$, so I know $7 - 4 = \blacksquare$.
- ○ 8
- ○ 5
- ● 3
- ○ 2

ACTIVITY How Many?

1. Take some red cubes.
   Write the number of red cubes. _____
   Answers will vary. Possible answer: 3

2. Take some blue cubes.
   Write the number of blue cubes. _____
   Answers will vary. Possible answer: 4

3. Draw to show the red cubes and blue cubes.
   Check children's drawings.

4. Write an equation that shows
   how many cubes in all.

   _____ + _____ = _____
   Answers will vary. Possible answer: 3 + 4 = 7

5. Tell how you added the cubes.
   Responses will indicate an understanding of the
   addition method the child used.

6. Write a subtraction equation.
   Make a Proof Drawing to solve it.

   _____ – _____ = _____
   Possible answer: 7 – 4 = 3. Check children's drawings.

7. Tell how you subtracted the circles.
   Responses will indicate an understanding of the
   subtraction method the child used.

Name

Count on to find the unknown partner.

1. $2 + \boxed{3} = 5$ **2.** $\boxed{3} + 4 = 7$ **3.** $\boxed{4} + 5 = 9$

Count on to solve.

4. 7 pencils total

How many pencils are in the box?

$\boxed{5}$ ___pencils___
label

5. 10 pennies total

How many pennies are
in the box?

$\boxed{7}$ ___pennies___
label

Name

Subtract.

1. $6 - 3 = \boxed{3}$ **2.** $7 - 2 = \boxed{5}$ **3.** $10 - 4 = \boxed{6}$

Solve the story problem.

Show your work.

4. Corey has 9 grapes.
He eats 5 of them.
How many grapes are left?

$\boxed{4}$ ___grapes___
label

5. There are 8 kittens.
6 kittens are black.
The rest are white.
How many kittens are white?

$\boxed{2}$ ___kittens___
label

Find the unknown partner or total. Watch the signs.

1. $6 - 5 = \boxed{1}$ | **2.** $8 + 2 = \boxed{10}$ | **3.** $7 - \boxed{6} = 1$

Show your work.

Solve the story problem.

4. Kyle catches 8 frogs.
He lets some frogs go.
Now Kyle has 2 frogs left.
How many frogs did he let go?

$\boxed{6}$
frogs
label

5. Some birds were in a tree. 4 birds flew away.
Then there were 5 birds. How many birds
were in the tree before?

$\boxed{9}$
birds
label

Write the correct answer.

Find the unknown partner or total. Watch the signs.

1. $6 + 2 = \boxed{8}$ | **2.** $4 + 3 = \boxed{7}$

3. $5 + \boxed{4} = 9$ | **4.** $3 + \boxed{7} = 10$

5. $8 - 5 = \boxed{3}$ | **6.** $9 - 3 = \boxed{6}$

7. $10 - \boxed{4} = 6$ | **8.** $10 - \boxed{8} = 2$

Show your work.

Solve the story problem.

9. Cal has 4 blue marbles
and 4 yellow marbles.
How many marbles does he have in all?

$\boxed{8}$
marbles
label

10. There are 3 seagulls on the shore.
Then 7 more seagulls come.
How many seagulls are there in all?

$\boxed{10}$
seagulls
label

Name _____

Solve the story problem.

Show your work.

11. Maisy has 5 red balloons.
She has some blue balloons.
Altogether she has 9 balloons.
How many blue balloons does Maisy have?

[4] __blue balloons__
          label

12. There are 3 ducks in the pond.
Then 5 more ducks come.
How many ducks are there now?

[8] __ducks__
          label

13. Anna sees 6 bees on a hive.
Some more bees join them.
Now there are 10 bees.
How many bees join?

[4] __bees__
          label

14. Avery has 7 baseball cards.
Jay gives him some more baseball cards.
Now Avery has 10 baseball cards.
How many baseball cards did Jay give Avery?

[3] __baseball cards__
          label

Name _____

Solve the story problem.

Show your work.

15. Lila has 10 books.
She gives 4 books away.
How many books are left?

[6] __books__
          label

16. Tom picks 8 apples.
He gives some away.
Now he has 5 apples.
How many apples did Tom give away?

[3] __apples__
          label

17. There are 9 fish. Then some
swim away. Now there are 3 fish.
How many fish swam away?

[6] __fish__
          label

18. There are 10 puppies.
7 puppies are sleeping.
How many puppies are not sleeping?

[3] __puppies__
          label

Unit 3 Test Form B

Fill in the ○ for the correct answer.

What is the unknown partner or total? Watch the signs.

1. 5 + 3 = ▩
- ○ 2
- ○ 7
- ● 8
- ○ 9

2. 7 + 2 = ▩
- ○ 5
- ○ 7
- ○ 8
- ● 9

3. 6 + ▩ = 10
- ● 4
- ○ 5
- ○ 6
- ○ 16

4. 4 + ▩ = 9
- ○ 3
- ○ 4
- ● 5
- ○ 13

5. 10 − 2 = ▩
- ○ 6
- ● 8
- ○ 10
- ○ 12

6. 8 − 4 = ▩
- ○ 2
- ○ 3
- ● 4
- ○ 12

Solve the story problem.   Show your work.

19. Marty sees 8 birds at the feeder.
There are red birds and blue birds.
How many of each color bird could Marty see?
Show three answers.

Answers will vary.
Sample answers are given.

[5] red birds and [3] blue birds

or [4] red birds and [4] blue birds

or [6] red birds and [2] blue birds

20. Extended Response Read the story problem. Write a subtraction and an addition equation for the story. Complete the Math Mountain to match.

There are 7 leaves on the branch. 3 leaves fall off. How many leaves are on the branch now?

Sample answers are given.

7 − 3 = [4]

3 + [4] = 7

[4] leaves are on the branch now.

7. 9 − ▓ = 4

- ○ 4
- ● 5
- ○ 8
- ○ 13

8. 10 − ▓ = 5

- ○ 15
- ○ 6
- ● 5
- ○ 1

Show your work.

Solve the story problem.

9. Jane sees 5 horses in the field and 4 horses in the barn. How many horses does Jane see in all?

- ● 9
- ○ 8
- ○ 4
- ○ 1

10. 7 children are on the playground. 3 more children join them. How many children are there in all?

- ○ 3
- ○ 4
- ○ 9
- ● 10

Solve the story problem.

Show your work.

11. Scott picks 8 red apples. He picks some green apples. Now he has 10 apples. How many green apples does Scott pick?

- ○ 1
- ● 2
- ○ 4
- ○ 18

12. There are 2 ants. Then 7 more ants join them. How many ants are there now?

- ○ 5
- ○ 8
- ● 9
- ○ 10

13. There are 4 butterflies. Some more butterflies join them. Now there are 10 butterflies. How many butterflies join?

- ○ 5
- ● 6
- ○ 12
- ○ 14

Solve the story problem.

Show your work.

14. Nina has 5 pennies. Pete gives her some more pennies. Now Nina has 9 pennies. How many pennies does Pete give her?

○ 14
○ 12
○ 9
● 4

15. Mike has 8 bananas. He eats 3 of them. How many bananas are left?

○ 4
● 5
○ 10
○ 11

16. Megan sees 10 ladybugs. Then 2 ladybugs fly away. How many ladybugs are left?

● 8
○ 9
○ 11
○ 12

Solve the story problem.

Show your work.

17. There are 8 turtles. Then some turtles swim away. Now there are 4 turtles. How many turtles swim away?

○ 12
○ 10
● 4
○ 3

18. There are 9 muffins. 6 muffins do not have raisins. How many muffins have raisins?

○ 15
○ 12
○ 5
● 3

ACTIVITY Hide and Seek

Some children are playing hide and seek.
Choose one of these numbers for each ○.

3 4 5 7

Solve the story problems.

1. 10 children are playing. ○ go and hide.   Possible responses: 6; 4 children
How many are left?

[□] ○
___label___

2. ○ children are hiding. ○ more children   Possible responses: 4; 5; 9 children
hide. How many children are hiding?

[□] ○
___label___

3. Write equations for Problems 1 and 2.

Possible responses: $10 - 6 = 4$; $4 + 5 = 9$

4. Show you know which partners and total to write in each equation.
Answers will vary.
Possible responses:

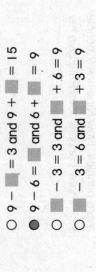

Solve the story problem.   Show your work.

19. Megan is putting 10 leaves on a board.
She has brown leaves and gold leaves.
Which shows the number of each color
leaf Megan could have?

○ 8 brown leaves and 1 gold leaf
○ 6 brown leaves and 3 gold leaves
○ 5 brown leaves and 4 gold leaves
● 4 brown leaves and 6 gold leaves

20. Read the story problem. Which shows
the subtraction and addition equations
for the story?

There are 9 books on a shelf.
Jose takes 6 of the books.
How many books are on the shelf now?

○ $9 - \blacksquare = 3$ and $9 + \blacksquare = 15$
● $9 - 6 = \blacksquare$ and $6 + \blacksquare = 9$
○ $\blacksquare - 3 = 3$ and $\blacksquare + 6 = 9$
○ $\blacksquare - 3 = 6$ and $\blacksquare + 3 = 9$

Name _____

Find the total. Then make a ten.

1. $7 + 5 = \boxed{12}$

   $10 + \boxed{2} = \boxed{12}$

2. $2 + 9 = \boxed{11}$

   $10 + \boxed{1} = \boxed{11}$

Use doubles or doubles plus 1 to find the total.

3. $6 + 6 = \boxed{12}$ 4. $9 + 8 = \boxed{17}$ 5. $8 + 7 = \boxed{15}$

Name _____

Write the numbers.

1. _____
   _____
   _____
   _____
   $\underline{4}$ tens $\underline{0}$ ones $= \underline{40}$

2. _____
   ○ ○
   $\underline{1}$ ten $\underline{2}$ ones $= \underline{12}$

Compare the numbers. Write >, <, or =.

3. $63 \;\textcircled{<}\; 73$ 4. $42 \;\textcircled{>}\; 24$ 5. $20 \;\textcircled{=}\; 20$

194

Name _____

Add.

1. $20 + 50 = \boxed{70}$

2. $60 + 30 = \boxed{90}$

Find the total.

3. $44 + 3 = \boxed{47}$

4. $72 + 9 = \boxed{81}$

Show your work.

Solve the story problem.

5. Cindy has 56 stamps.
   She buys 4 more stamps.
   How many stamps does she have now?

   $\boxed{60}$ _____ stamps

   _____ label

66

Name _____

Write the correct answer.

Write the numbers.

1. ○ ○ ○ _____

   $\underline{1}$ ten $\underline{3}$ ones = $\underline{13}$

2. _____
   _____

   $\underline{6}$ tens $\underline{0}$ ones = $\underline{60}$

Draw 10-sticks and circles.

3. 32   ○ ○

4. 64   ○ ○ ○ ○

5. Add 1 ten.

   $30 + 10 = \boxed{40}$

6. How many paper clips?

   $\boxed{17}$

67

How many jars are there?

7.

10   10

24

8.

10   10

10   10

41

Count on, make a ten, or use doubles.
Find the total.

9. $6 + 5 =$ 11

10. $9 + 4 =$ 13

Compare the numbers.
Write >, <, or =.

11. 42 $<$ 51

12. 65 $=$ 65

13. 87 $>$ 86

14. 34 $>$ 14

Solve the story problem.

Show your work.

15. There are 7 marbles in a jar
and 4 marbles beside the jar.
How many marbles are there?

11   marbles
       label

16. Meg has 8 red apples and
5 green apples. How many
apples does she have?

13   apples
       label

17. There are 9 books on the
shelf. Steve adds 7 more books.
How many books are there now?

16   books
       label

Find the total.

18. $14 + 3 = \boxed{17}$

19. $17 + 6 = \boxed{23}$

20. $24 + 8 = \boxed{32}$

21. $58 + 2 = \boxed{60}$

Solve to complete the set of exercises.

22. $6 + 2 = \boxed{8}$

23. $60 + 20 = \boxed{80}$

24. $60 + 2 = \boxed{62}$

25. Extended Response Write a number from 10 to 40. Add 1 ten. Write the new number. Draw and write to compare the numbers.

Answers and drawings will vary.

Fill in the ○ for the correct answer.

Which does the drawing show?

1. | ° ° ° ° °

- ○ 1 ten 4 ones = 14
- ● 1 ten 5 ones = 15
- ○ 5 tens 1 one = 51
- ○ 5 tens 2 ones = 52

2.

- ○ 6 tens 0 ones = 60
- ○ 5 tens 5 ones = 55
- ● 5 tens 0 ones = 50
- ○ 0 tens 5 ones = 5

Which shows 10-sticks and circles for the number?

3. 53

● ○ ○ ○

4. 21

○ ○ ○ ●

5. Which equation does the picture show?

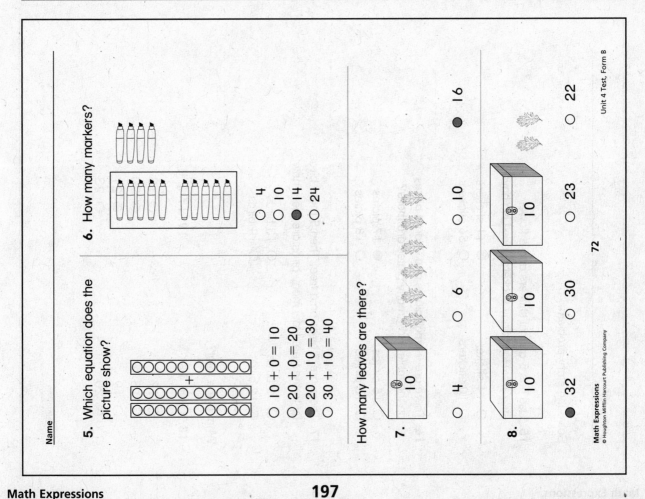

○ 10 + 0 = 10
○ 20 + 0 = 20
● 20 + 10 = 30
○ 30 + 10 = 40

6. How many markers?

○ 4
○ 10
● 14
○ 24

How many leaves are there?

7.

○ 4
○ 6
○ 10
● 16

8.

● 32
○ 30
○ 23
○ 22

Count on, make a ten, or use doubles.
What is the total?

9. 8 + 9 = ☐
○ 16
● 17
○ 18
○ 19

10. 7 + 4 = ☐
● 11
○ 12
○ 3
○ 10

Which is true?

11.
○ 27 = 17
● 27 > 17
○ 27 < 17
○ 17 > 27

12.
○ 80 < 79
○ 79 > 80
○ 79 = 80
● 80 > 79

13.
● 38 = 38
○ 38 < 38
○ 38 > 38
○ 38 = 83

14.
○ 45 > 54
● 45 < 54
○ 45 = 54
○ 54 < 45

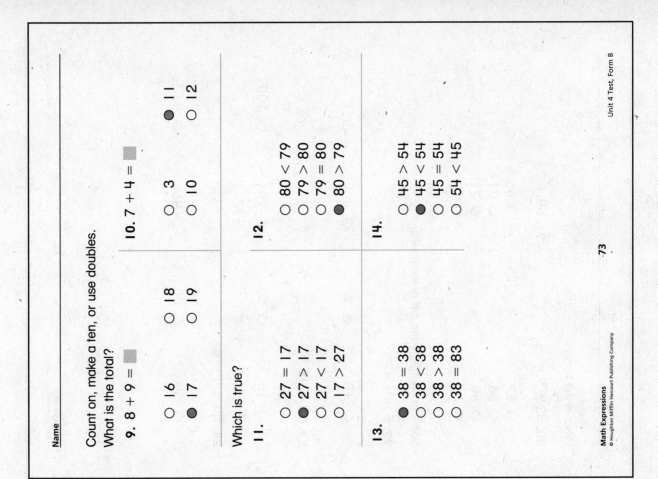

Solve the story problem.

Show your work.

15. Lisa has 5 animal stickers and 6 flower stickers. How many stickers does Lisa have?
- ○ 1 sticker
- ● 11 stickers
- ○ 10 stickers
- ○ 56 stickers

16. There are 9 small plates and 8 large plates on the table. How many plates are there?
- ○ 15 plates
- ○ 16 plates
- ● 17 plates
- ○ 18 plates

17. There are 7 birds on a tree. Then 5 more birds fly to the tree. How many birds are there now?
- ○ 2 birds
- ● 12 birds
- ○ 13 birds
- ○ 14 birds

What is the total?

18. 19 + 1 =
- ○ 17
- ○ 18
- ○ 19
- ● 20

19. 17 + 4 =
- ○ 13
- ○ 20
- ● 21
- ○ 23

What is the total?

20. 52 + 9 =
- ○ 57
- ○ 58
- ○ 60
- ● 61

21. 69 + 3 =
- ○ 66
- ○ 71
- ● 72
- ○ 74

Solve to complete the set of exercises.

22. 5 + 4 =
- ○ 10
- ● 9
- ○ 8
- ○ 1

23. 50 + 40 =
- ○ 10
- ○ 80
- ● 90
- ○ 100

24. 50 + 4 =
- ● 54
- ○ 50
- ○ 46
- ○ 44

ACTIVITY Snack Time

It is snack time. The class has these drinks.

Milk		Juice	
Chocolate Milk	Strawberry Milk	Orange Juice	Apple Juice
13 cartons	11 cartons	9 boxes	7 boxes

1. Are there more cartons of chocolate milk or strawberry milk? How do you know? Chocolate milk; responses should indicate an understanding of place value in 2-digit number comparison.

2. Ring one kind of milk. Draw 10-sticks and circles to show the number. Children should ring one kind of milk and show the number with 10-sticks and circles.

3. Are there enough juice boxes for 16 children? How do you know? Write or draw the answer. Yes; Answers will vary but should include adding 9 + 7 to find 16.

4. There are 20 children in a class. Each chooses one drink. Show one way children could choose drinks. Children should show numbers of two or more kinds of drinks that total 20.

Drink	How many?
Chocolate Milk	
Strawberry Milk	
Orange Juice	
Apple Juice	

---

25. Eric wrote the number 43. Then he added 1 ten. He compared the two numbers. Which shows how Eric should compare the numbers?

○ 33 < 43
○ 43 < 44
○ 33 < 53
● 43 < 53

Use the grid.

51	52	53	54	55	56	57	58	59	60
61	62	63	64	65	66	67	68	69	70
71	72	73	74	75	76	77	78	79	80

1. 10 more than 54 is 64 .

2. 10 more than 68 is 78 .

Add or subtract tens.

3. $68 + 30 = 98$

4. $52 + 20 = 72$

5. $80 - 50 = 30$

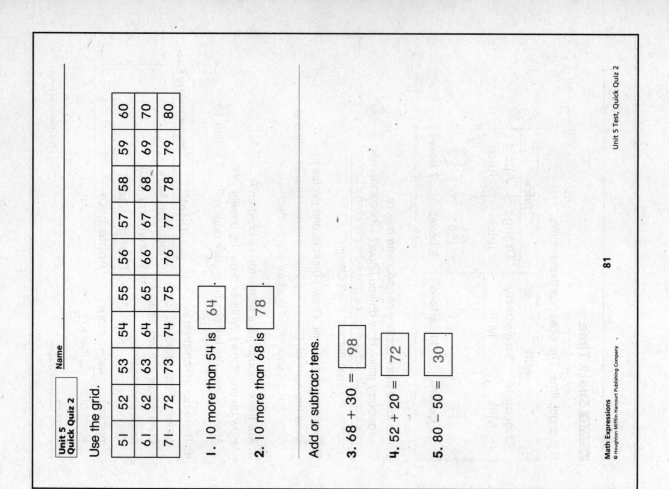

Add or subtract.

1. $9 + 8 = 17$

2. $15 - 8 = 7$

3. $7 + 9 = 16$

Show your work.

Solve the story problem.

4. There are 14 ants. 9 ants are red and the rest are black. How many ants are black?

5 ants
label

5. Bailey found 4 clam shells, 5 snail shells, and 6 scallop shells. How many shells did she find in all?

15 shells
label

Name _____

Write the correct answer.

Add.

1. $9 + \boxed{6} = 15$

2. $8 + \boxed{9} = 17$

3. $8 + \boxed{6} = 14$

Subtract.

4. $14 - 8 = \boxed{6}$

5. $16 - 7 = \boxed{9}$

6. $17 - 9 = \boxed{8}$

Solve the story problem.   Show your work.

7. 14 birds sit on a tree. Some birds fly away.
Now there are 6 birds. How many birds
fly away?

$\boxed{8}$ _____ birds
          label

8. There are 15 squirrels. 6 are gray and the rest
are brown. How many squirrels are brown?

$\boxed{9}$ _____ squirrels
          label

Name _____

Solve the story problem.   Show your work.

9. Meg had 6 stickers. Jen gave her some more
stickers. Now Meg has 14 stickers. How many
stickers did Jen give Meg?

$\boxed{8}$ _____ stickers
          label

10. Beth makes 16 bracelets. She gives 8 to her
friends. How many bracelets does Beth
have now?

$\boxed{8}$ _____ bracelets
          label

11. Max has 7 blue marbles, 4 red marbles, and
3 green marbles. How many marbles does
Max have?

$\boxed{14}$ _____ marbles
          label

12. There are 9 red crayons, 3 green crayons, and
7 blue crayons in the box. How many crayons
are in the box?

$\boxed{19}$ _____ crayons
          label

24. Start at 81. Count. Write the numbers through 110.

81	82	83	84	85	86	87	88	89	90
91	92	93	94	95	96	97	98	99	100
101	102	103	104	105	106	107	108	109	110

25. Extended Response Draw 10 to 20 more triangles. Ring 10-groups. Count by tens and ones. Write the numbers.

Possible response shown.

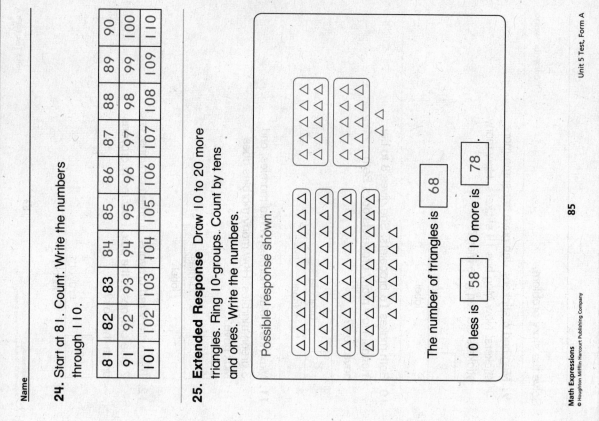

The number of triangles is 68 .

10 less is 58 . 10 more is 78 .

Solve the story problem.   Show your work.

13. There are 12 boys and girls on the bus. How many boys and girls could there be? Show three answers.

Answers will vary.
Sample answers are given.

    2 boys and 10 girls

or 3 boys and 9 girls

or 4 boys and 8 girls

Solve.

14. 80 + 20 = 100

15. 40 + 60 = 100

16. 57 + 20 = 77

17. 40 + 24 = 64

18. 80 - 40 = 40

19. 70 - 30 = 40

20. 60 - 60 = 0

21. 40 - 0 = 40

22. 70 - 40 = 30

23. 80 - 10 = 70

    30 + 40 = 70

    70 + 10 = 80

Name _____

Fill in the ○ for the correct answer.

Add.

1. $7 + \blacksquare = 13$

○ 4   ● 6   ○ 8   ○ 20

2. $7 + \blacksquare = 15$

○ 6   ○ 7   ● 8   ○ 9

3. $9 + \blacksquare = 16$

○ 6   ● 7   ○ 8   ○ 9

Subtract.

4. $15 - 6 = \blacksquare$

● 9   ○ 11   ○ 8   ○ 7

5. $13 - 8 = \blacksquare$

● 5   ○ 6   ○ 11   ○ 15

6. $16 - 8 = \blacksquare$

○ 6   ○ 7   ○ 4   ● 8

Name _____

Solve the story problem.   Show your work.

7. There are 14 leaves on a tree. Some leaves fall. Now there are 8 leaves on the tree. How many leaves fell?

○ 12   ● 6   ○ 10   ○ 4

8. There are 11 fish. 2 are blue and the rest are orange. How many fish are orange?

○ 7   ● 9   ○ 8   ○ 11

9. Toby had 3 books. Jim gave him some more books. Now Toby has 11 books. How many books did Jim give Toby?

○ 6   ○ 9   ● 8   ○ 11

10. Beth makes 16 snacks. She gives 8 snacks to her friends. How many snacks does Beth have now?

○ 12   ○ 9   ○ 10   ● 8

Solve.

15. 50 + ▢ = 100

- ○ 30
- ○ 40
- ● 50
- ○ 60

17. 50 + 17 = ▢

- ○ 63
- ● 67
- ○ 72
- ○ 77

19. 80 − 70 = ▢

- ● 10
- ○ 20
- ○ 40
- ○ 50

14. 70 + ▢ = 80

- ○ 40
- ○ 30
- ○ 20
- ● 10

16. 81 + 10 = ▢

- ○ 70
- ○ 71
- ○ 90
- ● 91

18. 60 − 10 = ▢

- ○ 40
- ● 50
- ○ 60
- ○ 70

Solve the story problem.

Show your work.

11. Jude has 8 green blocks,
4 red blocks, and 2 green blocks.
How many blocks does Jude have?

- ○ 12
- ○ 13
- ● 14
- ○ 15

12. David has 6 red markers,
5 green markers, and 7 blue markers.
How many markers does David have?

- ○ 19
- ○ 17
- ● 18
- ○ 16

13. There are 13 mice in the cage.
Some are brown and some are white.
Which shows the number of brown mice
and white mice that could be in the cage?

- ● 9 brown and 4 white
- ○ 9 brown and 3 white
- ○ 8 brown and 4 white
- ○ 8 brown and 3 white

20. 90 − 90 = ▨

○ 0 ●
● 10 ○
○ 80
○ 90

22. Which number makes both equations true?

90 − ▨ = 40
40 + ▨ = 90

○ 30
○ 40
● 50
○ 60

21. 70 − 0 = ▨

○ 0
○ 7
○ 10
● 70

23. Which number makes both equations true?

60 − ▨ = 40
40 + ▨ = 60

● 20
○ 30
○ 40
○ 100

---

24. Start at 71. Count through 100. Which number is missing?

71	72	73	74	75	76	77	78	79	80
81	82	83	84	85	86	▨	88	89	90
91	92	93	94	95	96	97	98	99	100

○ 78
○ 86
● 87
○ 97

25. Which number is 10 more than the number of circles?

○ 39
○ 40
● 49
○ 50

ACTIVITY **Beach Day**

Dan and Win look for shells at the beach.

1. Dan finds 32 shells. Make a drawing to
show 32 with tens and ones.
Children should show the number with 10-sticks and
circles or other ways that clearly show tens and ones.

2. Dan finds 20 more shells. How many shells does   Show your work.
he have in all?

[52] __shells__
__label__

3. Win finds 8 white shells, 4 brown shells, and 2   Show your work.
black shells. How many shells does she have in all?

[14] __shells__
__label__

4. Win found 80 white shells, 40 brown shells, and
20 black shells. How would you find out how many
shells she has in all?
Responses should indicate an understanding of
place value and the similarity between Problems 3
and 4.

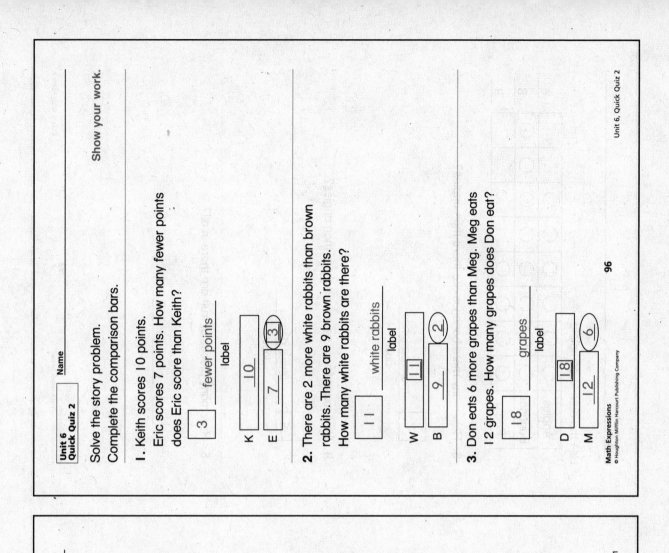

Unit 6 Quick Quiz 1

Name _____

1. How many in each group?

Pencils	●	●	●	●	●	●			6
Crayons	●	●	●	●	●	●	●	●	8
Markers	●	●							2

Use the data to complete each sentence.

2. There are ⊡4 more pencils than markers.

3. There are ⊡2 more crayons than pencils.

4. There are ⊡6 fewer markers than crayons.

5. There are ⊡2 fewer pencils than crayons.

Unit 6 Quick Quiz 2

Name _____   Show your work.

Solve the story problem.
Complete the comparison bars.

1. Keith scores 10 points.
Eric scores 7 points. How many fewer points
does Eric score than Keith?

⊡3 _____ fewer points
              label

| K | 10 |
| E | 7 | ③ |

2. There are 2 more white rabbits than brown
rabbits. There are 9 brown rabbits.
How many white rabbits are there?

⊡11 _____ white rabbits
              label

| W | 11 |
| B | 9 | 2 |

3. Don eats 6 more grapes than Meg. Meg eats
12 grapes. How many grapes does Don eat?

⊡18 _____ grapes
              label

| D | 18 |
| M | 12 | 6 |

Name _____

Use the data to complete.

Apples	○	○	○	○	○	○			6
Bananas	○	○	○	○	○	○	○	○	8
Pears	○	○	○	○					4

3. How many more bananas are there than apples?

[2] _____ more bananas
        label

4. How many fewer pears are there than apples?

[2] _____ fewer pears
        label

5. How many pieces of fruit are there in all?

[18] _____ pieces of fruit
        label

Name _____

Write the correct answer.

1. Sort the animals. Record with circles.

2. Write how many in each group.

Cats	○	○	○	○	○	○	○		7
Dogs	○	○	○	○	○	○	○	○	8
Birds	○	○	○	○	○				5

Name _____

Solve the story problem.
Use comparison bars.   **Show your work.**

9. Steve has 9 more pencils than markers.
He has 8 markers.
How many pencils does Steve have?

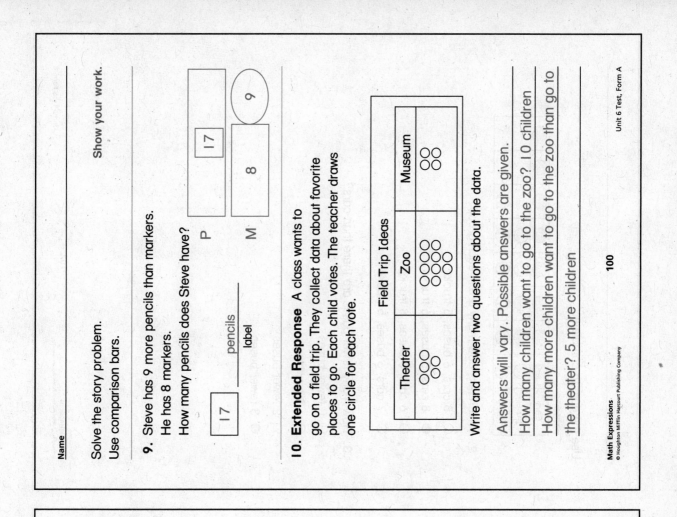

P	17	9
M	8

$\boxed{17}$ __pencils__
         label

10. Extended Response A class wants to go on a field trip. They collect data about favorite places to go. Each child draws one circle for each vote. The teacher draws one circle for each vote.

Field Trip Ideas

Theater	Zoo	Museum
○○○ ○○	○○○○ ○○○ ○	○○

Write and answer two questions about the data.

Answers will vary. Possible answers are given.

How many children want to go to the zoo? 10 children

How many more children want to go to the zoo than go to the theater? 5 more children

---

Name _____

Solve the story problem.
Use comparison bars.   **Show your work.**

6. Kris has 15 coins.
Carol has 6 coins.
How many more coins does Kris have than Carol?

K	15	
C	6	9

$\boxed{9}$ __more coins__
         label

7. Rich sees 5 more cats than dogs.
He sees 12 cats.
How many dogs does he see?

C	12	
D	7	5

$\boxed{7}$ __dogs__
         label

8. Joy picks 13 tulips.
Emily picks 8 tulips.
How many fewer tulips does Emily pick than Joy?

J	13	
E	8	5

$\boxed{5}$ __fewer tulips__
         label

Use the data to complete.

Cars	●	●	●	●	●	●	●	●	
Buses			●	●	●	●	●	●	
Trucks			●	●	●	●	●	●	

2. Which tells how many are in each group?

○ 8 cars, 6 buses, 5 trucks

● 8 cars, 5 buses, 6 trucks

○ 6 cars, 5 buses, 6 trucks

○ 7 cars, 6 buses, 5 trucks

3. How many fewer buses are there than cars?

○ 0 fewer buses

○ 1 fewer bus

○ 2 fewer buses

● 3 fewer buses

Fill in the ○ for the correct answer.

1. Which table shows the correct way to sort the fruit?

○

○

●

Use the data to complete.

Cars	○	○	○	○	○	○	○	○	○
Buses	○	○	○	○	○				
Trucks	○	○	○	○	○	○			

4. How many more trucks are there than buses?

● 1 more truck
○ 2 more trucks
○ 3 more trucks
○ 4 more trucks

5. How many vehicles are there in all?

○ 18 vehicles
● 19 vehicles
○ 20 vehicles
○ 21 vehicles

Solve the story problem.
Use the comparison bars to help you.

Show your work.

6. Keegan read 8 books.
Ann read 12 books.
How many more books did
Ann read than Keegan?

A	12

K	8	?

○ 3 more books
● 4 more books
○ 6 more books
○ 20 more books

7. There are 5 more bran muffins
than apple muffins. There are
16 bran muffins. How many
apple muffins are there?

B	16

A	?	5

○ 21 apple muffins
○ 18 apple muffins
○ 15 apple muffins
● 11 apple muffins

10. Wendy's class votes for their favorite pizza. The teacher draws one circle for each vote.

Favorite Pizza		
Cheese	Pepperoni	Veggie

Which question could be answered about the data?

○ How many children like mushroom pizza?

○ How many fewer children like cheese pizza than veggie pizza?

○ How many more children like veggie pizza than pepperoni pizza?

● How many children like pepperoni pizza?

Solve the story problem.
Use the comparison bars to help you.

Show your work.

8. Jim counts 18 pine trees. He counts 9 birch trees. How many fewer birch trees than pine trees does Jim count?

P	18
B	9	?

○ 7 fewer birch trees

○ 8 fewer birch trees

● 9 fewer birch trees

○ 10 fewer birch trees

9. There are 3 more apple pies than peach pies. There are 8 peach pies. How many apple pies are there?

A	?
P	8	3

○ 5 apple pies

○ 7 apple pies

○ 9 apple pies

● 11 apple pies

Name

ACTIVITY Sort and Compare

Use the strips of paper for this activity.

1. Sort the strips. Draw 5-groups and circles in the table to show how many strips there are of each color.

Children should draw 5-groups and circles in the table to correctly represent the color strips they have.

My Color Strips

Red	Blue	Yellow

2. How many strips are red? Answers will vary but will indicate the number of red strips.

[ ]
label

3. How many strips are **not** blue? How do you know?
Answers will vary but should indicate the number of red and yellow strips altogether.

4. How many more strips are there of the color with the most strips than the color with the fewest strips?

Answers will vary but should indicate the difference between the color with the most strips and the color with the fewest strips.

[ ]
label

5. Write 2 sentences about the data.
Responses should indicate an understanding of the relationships among the number of red, blue, and yellow strips.

Unit 7
Quick Quiz 2

1. Draw an X on the shape that is NOT a square.

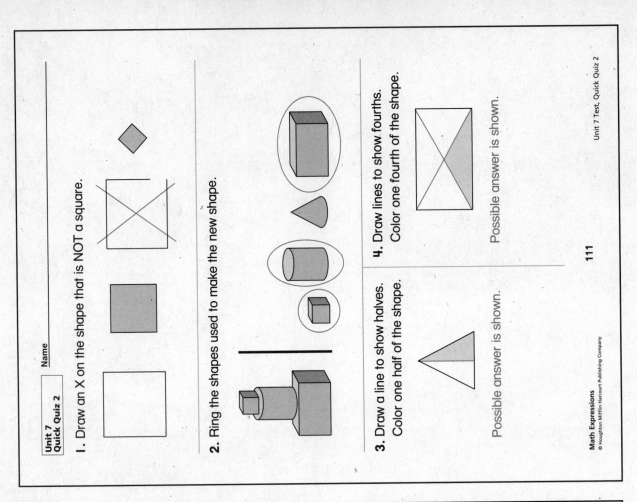

2. Ring the shapes used to make the new shape.

3. Draw a line to show halves.
Color one half of the shape.

Possible answer is shown.

4. Draw lines to show fourths.
Color one fourth of the shape.

Possible answer is shown.

Unit 7
Quick Quiz 1

Read the clock.
Write the time on the digital clock.

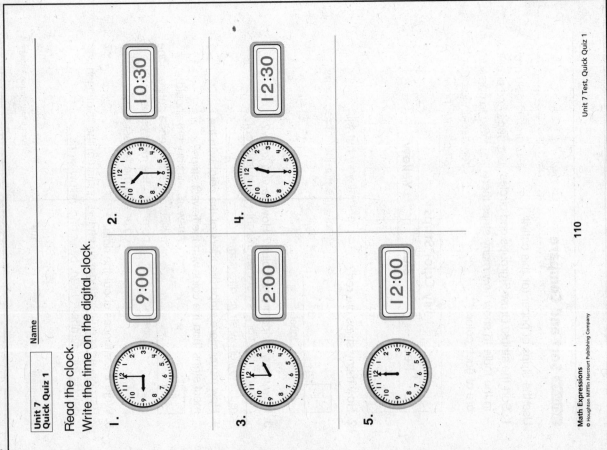

1. 9:00

2. 10:30

3. 2:00

4. 12:30

5. 12:00

Write the correct answer.

Read the clock.
Write the time on the digital clock.

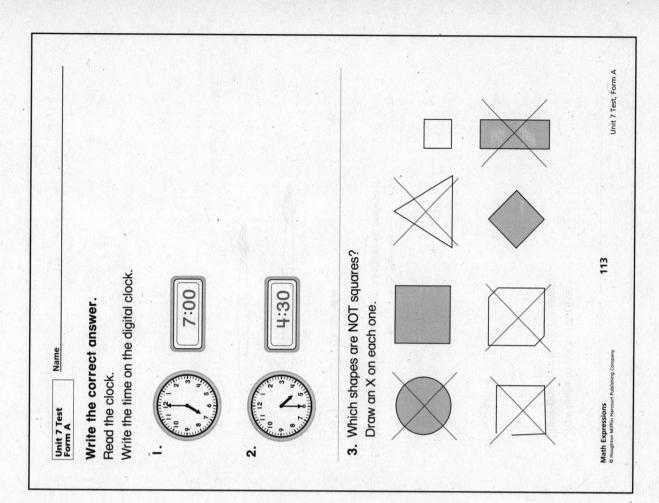

1. **7:00**

2. **4:30**

3. Which shapes are NOT squares?
    Draw an X on each one.

Write 1, 2, 3 in order from longest to shortest.

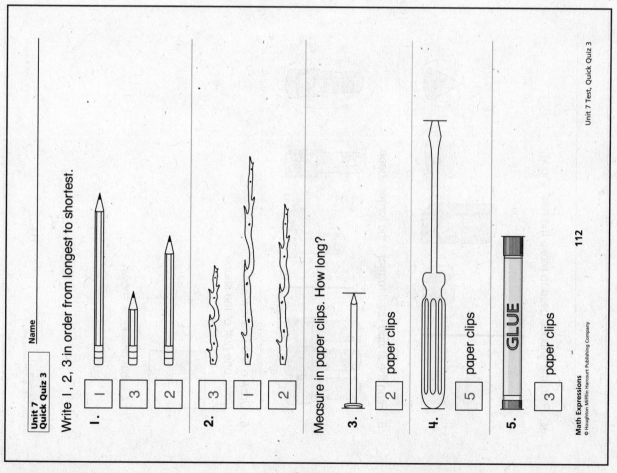

1. 1
    3
    2

2. 3
    1
    2

Measure in paper clips. How long?

3. **2** paper clips

4. **5** paper clips

5. GLUE
    3 paper clips

7. Draw lines to show fourths.
Color one fourth of the shape.

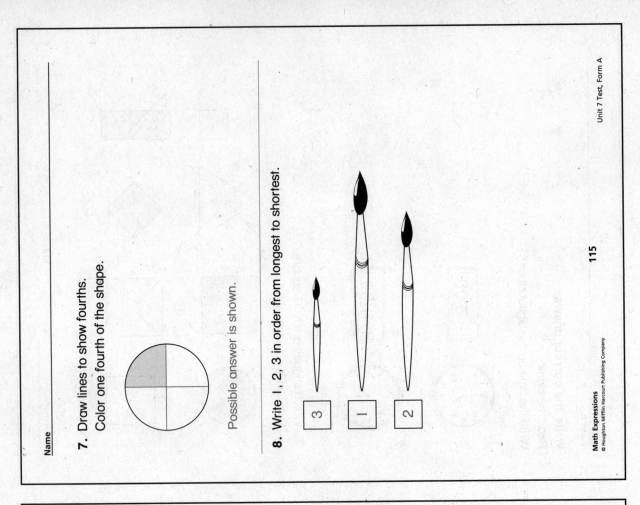

Possible answer is shown.

8. Write 1, 2, 3 in order from longest to shortest.

3

1

2

---

4. Ring the shapes used to make the new shape.

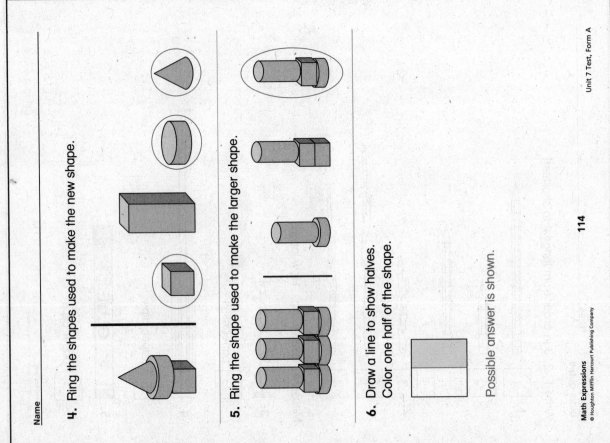

5. Ring the shape used to make the larger shape.

6. Draw a line to show halves.
Color one half of the shape.

Possible answer is shown.

9. Measure in paper clips.

How long? 3 paper clips

10. **Extended Response** Mason has this piece of chalk and this marker.

Deann gives him a pen that is longer than the marker. Is the pen longer than the chalk? Explain.

Yes: possible explanation: since the marker is longer than the chalk, and the pen is longer than the marker, the pen is longer than the chalk.

Fill in the ○ for the correct answer.

Read the clock.
What time does the clock show?

1.

○ 3:00   ● 5:00

○ 4:00   ○ 6:00

2.

○ 12:30   ○ 2:30

● 1:30   ○ 6:30

---

5. Which shape was used to make the larger shape?

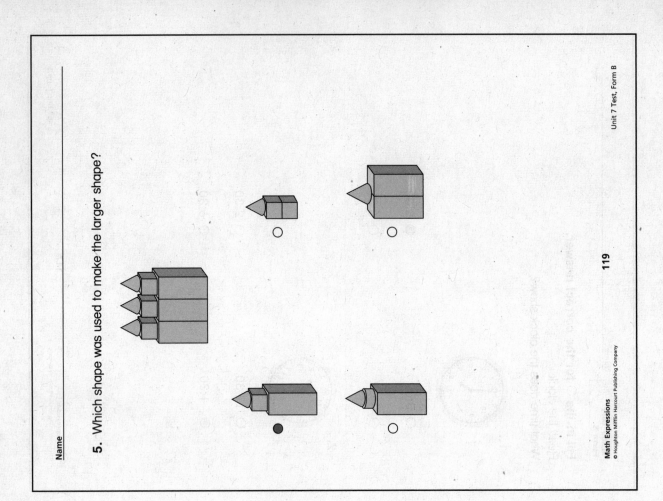

3. Which shape is NOT a triangle?

4. Which shape was NOT used to make the new shape?

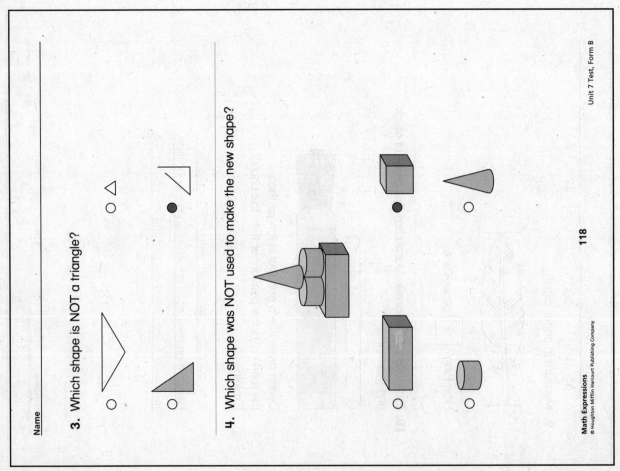

Name _____

8. Which shows the strings in order from shortest to longest?

9. Measure in paper clips. How long is the eraser?

○ 1 paper clip

● 2 paper clips

○ 3 paper clips

○ 4 paper clips

Name _____

6. Which circle shows halves?

7. Which shows one fourth of the square shaded?

ACTIVITY Busy Bug's Bedtime

1. This is Busy Bug's bedtime.

Write the time on the digital clock to show Busy Bug's bedtime.

7:30

2. This is Busy Bug's snack. He wants to share it with Sleepy Spider.

Draw a line to show halves. Color half of the shape

Children divide the rectangle into halves horizontally, vertically, or diagonally. Some may draw a curved line.

3. This is Busy Bug's bed.

How many paper clips long is it?

2 paper clips

_____ label

4. Find objects longer and shorter than Busy Bug's bed. Draw and label a picture of all three in order by length.

Drawings will vary. Each child's measurements and order should match his or her drawing and labels.

---

10. Jack has a baseball bat and a tennis racket.

Lee has a hockey stick that is longer than Jack's baseball bat.

Which is true?

○ The hockey stick is shorter than the tennis racket.

○ The baseball bat is longer than the hockey stick.

● The hockey stick is longer than the tennis racket.

○ The baseball bat is shorter than the tennis racket.

Unit 8
Quick Quiz 1

Add.

1. 27
    + 5
    —
    32

2. 43
    + 30
    —
    73

3. 65
    + 13
    —
    78

Write the vertical form. Then add.

4. 12 + 40

    12
    + 40
    —
    52

5. 38 + 6

    38
    + 6
    —
    44

Math Expressions
© Houghton Mifflin Harcourt Publishing Company

Unit 8 Test
Form A

Write the correct answer.

Add.

1. 63
    + 29
    —
    92

2. 52
    + 23
    —
    75

3. 46
    + 9
    —
    55

4. 35
    + 20
    —
    55

Math Expressions
© Houghton Mifflin Harcourt Publishing Company

Write the vertical form. Then add.

5. $51 + 40$

$$\begin{array}{r} 51 \\ +40 \\ \hline 91 \end{array}$$

6. $47 + 12$

$$\begin{array}{r} 47 \\ +12 \\ \hline 59 \end{array}$$

7. $57 + 15$

$$\begin{array}{r} 57 \\ +15 \\ \hline 72 \end{array}$$

8. $82 + 6$

$$\begin{array}{r} 82 \\ +6 \\ \hline 88 \end{array}$$

Show your work.

Solve the story problem.

9. How many apples are there in all? Show your work.

54 apples   29 apples

83

apples

label

$$\begin{array}{r} 54 \\ +29 \\ \hline 83 \end{array}$$

10. Extended Response Write an addition exercise that you must make a new ten to solve. Use two 2-digit numbers. Make a Proof Drawing.

Answers and drawings will vary.
Check children's work.

Name _____

Fill in the ○ for the correct answer.

Add.

1. 58
  + 32

○ 26
○ 80
○ 81
● 90

2. 24
  + 15

● 39
○ 38
○ 19
○ 11

3. 53
  + 8

○ 51
○ 55
● 61
○ 65

4. 49
  + 30

○ 69
● 79
○ 89
○ 99

Math Expressions
© Houghton Mifflin Harcourt Publishing Company

Name _____

Add.

5. 37 + 20 = ☐

○ 17
○ 39
○ 47
● 57

6. 25 + 44 = ☐

○ 21
● 69
○ 79
○ 96

7. 46 + 28 = ☐

○ 22
○ 64
● 74
○ 76

8. 55 + 4 = ☐

○ 51
● 59
○ 69
○ 95

Math Expressions
© Houghton Mifflin Harcourt Publishing Company

ACTIVITY Picking Pears

Write a 2-digit number in each ◯.
Explain how you solved the story problem.

Show your work.

Answers will vary but should include a method for adding a 2-digit number and a 1-digit number. Possible answer:
$12 + 9 = 21.$

1. Rena picks ◯ pears. Lisa picks 9 pears. How many pears do they pick in all?

[ ] _____
      label

Show your work.

Answers will vary but should include a method for adding a 2-digit number and a multiple of 10. Possible answer:
$45 + 20 = 65.$

2. Rena and Lisa pick ◯ pears. Then they pick 20 more pears. What is the total number of pears they picked?

[ ] _____
      label

Show your work.

Answers will vary but should include a method for adding two 2-digit numbers. Possible answer: $34 + 19 = 53.$

3. Rena and Lisa pick ◯ pears. How many pears do Rena and Lisa pick altogether if now they pick ◯ more?

[ ] _____
      label

4. If every 2-digit number in the problem ended in 0, would you solve it the same way? Explain.
Answer will vary but should include a method for adding multiples of 10.

Solve the story problem.   **Show your work.**

9. How many oranges are there in all?

38 oranges   36 oranges

◯ 62   ◯ 72

◯ 64   ● 74

10. Which addition exercise must you make a new ten to solve?

◯ 48 + 21   ◯ 27 + 10

◯ 64 + 35   ● 16 + 19

Fluency Check 1

PATH to FLUENCY

Add.

1. $2 + 0 = \boxed{2}$ 2. $0 + 4 = \boxed{4}$ 3. $7 + 0 = \boxed{7}$

4. $0 + 1 = \boxed{1}$ 5. $3 + 0 = \boxed{3}$ 6. $0 + 5 = \boxed{5}$

7. $9 + 0 = \boxed{9}$ 8. $0 + 8 = \boxed{8}$ 9. $6 + 0 = \boxed{6}$

10. $0 + 10 = \boxed{10}$ 11. $5 + 0 = \boxed{5}$ 12. $0 + 7 = \boxed{7}$

13. $8 + 0 = \boxed{8}$ 14. $0 + 9 = \boxed{9}$ 15. $10 + 0 = \boxed{10}$

Math Expressions
© Houghton Mifflin Harcourt Publishing Company

Fluency Check 1
Use after Lesson 2-4

Fluency Check 2

PATH to FLUENCY

Add.

1. $5 + 0 = \boxed{5}$ 2. $0 + 6 = \boxed{6}$ 3. $0 + 8 = \boxed{8}$

4. $9 + 0 = \boxed{9}$ 5. $0 + 10 = \boxed{10}$ 6. $9 + 1 = \boxed{10}$

7. $1 + 3 = \boxed{4}$ 8. $2 + 1 = \boxed{3}$ 9. $2 + 3 = \boxed{5}$

10. $1 + 5 = \boxed{6}$ 11. $4 + 0 = \boxed{4}$ 12. $7 + 1 = \boxed{8}$

13. $3 + 2 = \boxed{5}$ 14. $1 + 9 = \boxed{10}$ 15. $8 + 1 = \boxed{9}$

Math Expressions
© Houghton Mifflin Harcourt Publishing Company

Fluency Check 2
Use after Lesson 2-9

Math Expressions
© Houghton Mifflin Harcourt Publishing Company

Answer Key

PATH to FLUENCY   Fluency Check 3

Subtract.

1. $1 - 0 = \boxed{1}$ 2. $3 - 1 = \boxed{2}$ 3. $2 - 0 = \boxed{2}$

4. $4 - 1 = \boxed{3}$ 5. $6 - 0 = \boxed{6}$ 6. $5 - 1 = \boxed{4}$

7. $7 - 0 = \boxed{7}$ 8. $8 - 1 = \boxed{7}$ 9. $9 - 1 = \boxed{8}$

10. $8 - 0 = \boxed{8}$ 11. $9 - 0 = \boxed{9}$ 12. $7 - 1 = \boxed{6}$

13. $10 - 0 = \boxed{10}$ 14. $6 - 1 = \boxed{5}$ 15. $10 - 1 = \boxed{9}$

Fluency Check 3
Use after Lesson 2-13

Math Expressions
© Houghton Mifflin Harcourt Publishing Company

PATH to FLUENCY   Fluency Check 4

Subtract.

1. $1 - 1 = \boxed{0}$ 2. $2 - 0 = \boxed{2}$ 3. $2 - 1 = \boxed{1}$

4. $4 - 1 = \boxed{3}$ 5. $3 - 1 = \boxed{2}$ 6. $5 - 0 = \boxed{5}$

7. $3 - 2 = \boxed{1}$ 8. $5 - 1 = \boxed{4}$ 9. $6 - 0 = \boxed{6}$

10. $7 - 0 = \boxed{7}$ 11. $4 - 2 = \boxed{2}$ 12. $6 - 1 = \boxed{5}$

13. $8 - 1 = \boxed{7}$ 14. $9 - 0 = \boxed{9}$ 15. $5 - 2 = \boxed{3}$

Fluency Check 4
Use after Lesson 2-16

Math Expressions
© Houghton Mifflin Harcourt Publishing Company

PATH to FLUENCY

Fluency Check 5

Add.

1. $1 + 1 = \boxed{2}$

2. $2 + 8 = \boxed{10}$

3. $8 + 2 = \boxed{10}$

4. $3 + 7 = \boxed{10}$

5. $2 + 2 = \boxed{4}$

6. $1 + 9 = \boxed{10}$

7. $0 + 10 = \boxed{10}$

8. $4 + 6 = \boxed{10}$

9. $3 + 3 = \boxed{6}$

10. $9 + 1 = \boxed{10}$

11. $4 + 4 = \boxed{8}$

12. $6 + 4 = \boxed{10}$

13. $5 + 5 = \boxed{10}$

14. $10 + 0 = \boxed{10}$

15. $7 + 3 = \boxed{10}$

Math Expressions
© Houghton Mifflin Harcourt Publishing Company

Fluency Check 5
Use after Lesson 3-5

PATH to FLUENCY

Fluency Check 6

Subtract.

1. $2 - 1 = \boxed{1}$

2. $4 - 3 = \boxed{1}$

3. $3 - 2 = \boxed{1}$

4. $7 - 6 = \boxed{1}$

5. $6 - 5 = \boxed{1}$

6. $5 - 4 = \boxed{1}$

7. $9 - 8 = \boxed{1}$

8. $8 - 7 = \boxed{1}$

9. $10 - 9 = \boxed{1}$

10. $4 - 3 = \boxed{1}$

11. $6 - 5 = \boxed{1}$

12. $2 - 1 = \boxed{1}$

13. $5 - 4 = \boxed{1}$

14. $10 - 9 = \boxed{1}$

15. $7 - 6 = \boxed{1}$

Math Expressions
© Houghton Mifflin Harcourt Publishing Company

Fluency Check 6
Use after Lesson 3-8

Math Expressions
© Houghton Mifflin Harcourt Publishing Company

Answer Key

PATH to FLUENCY

Fluency Check 8

Subtract.

1. $6 - 2 = 4$
2. $8 - 1 = 7$
3. $7 - 0 = 7$
4. $8 - 4 = 4$
5. $7 - 3 = 4$
6. $6 - 3 = 3$
7. $9 - 4 = 5$
8. $6 - 5 = 1$
9. $7 - 2 = 5$
10. $10 - 5 = 5$
11. $9 - 6 = 3$
12. $10 - 2 = 8$
13. $9 - 7 = 2$
14. $10 - 9 = 1$
15. $8 - 5 = 3$

PATH to FLUENCY

Fluency Check 7

Subtract.

1. $2 - 1 = \boxed{1}$
2. $3 - 3 = \boxed{0}$
3. $1 - 1 = \boxed{0}$
4. $2 - 2 = \boxed{0}$
5. $4 - 2 = \boxed{2}$
6. $5 - 5 = \boxed{0}$
7. $7 - 7 = \boxed{0}$
8. $6 - 6 = \boxed{0}$
9. $6 - 3 = \boxed{3}$
10. $8 - 8 = \boxed{0}$
11. $8 - 4 = \boxed{4}$
12. $9 - 9 = \boxed{0}$
13. $10 - 10 = \boxed{0}$
14. $10 - 5 = \boxed{5}$
15. $4 - 4 = \boxed{0}$

Name _____ Date _____

PATH to FLUENCY

Fluency Check 10

Find the unknown partner or total.

1. $5 + 2 = \boxed{7}$
2. $1 + 5 = \boxed{6}$
3. $2 + 4 = \boxed{6}$

4. $5 + 4 = \boxed{9}$
5. $2 + 6 = \boxed{8}$
6. $5 + 5 = \boxed{10}$

7. $1 + \boxed{6} = 7$
8. $4 + \boxed{2} = 6$
9. $0 + 8 = 8$

10. $6 + \boxed{3} = 9$
11. $2 + \boxed{6} = 8$

12. $9 + \boxed{1} = 10$
13. $\boxed{3} + 3 = 6$

14. $\boxed{9} + 0 = 9$
15. $\boxed{1} + 7 = 8$

Fluency Check 10
Use after Lesson 4-18

Name _____ Date _____

PATH to FLUENCY

Fluency Check 9

Find the unknown partner or total.

1. $3 + 3 = \boxed{6}$
2. $4 + 2 = \boxed{6}$
3. $5 + 3 = \boxed{8}$

4. $3 + 4 = \boxed{7}$
5. $8 + 1 = \boxed{9}$
6. $2 + 5 = \boxed{7}$

7. $4 + \boxed{2} = 6$
8. $7 + \boxed{2} = 9$
9. $1 + \boxed{6} = 7$

10. $4 + \boxed{4} = 8$
11. $8 + \boxed{2} = 10$

12. $3 + \boxed{7} = 10$
13. $\boxed{6} + 3 = 9$

14. $\boxed{3} + 5 = 8$
15. $\boxed{6} + 4 = 10$

Fluency Check 9
Use after Lesson 4-12

Answer Key

Name _____

PATH to FLUENCY

Fluency Check 11

Subtract.

1. $7 - 2 = \boxed{5}$ 2. $6 - 1 = \boxed{5}$ 3. $7 - 4 = \boxed{3}$

4. $8 - 5 = \boxed{3}$ 5. $6 - 3 = \boxed{3}$ 6. $7 - 7 = \boxed{0}$

7. $8 - 7 = \boxed{1}$ 8. $9 - 6 = \boxed{3}$ 9. $6 - 5 = \boxed{1}$

10. $8 - 2 = \boxed{6}$ 11. $10 - 2 = \boxed{8}$ 12. $9 - 3 = \boxed{6}$

13. $10 - 10 = \boxed{0}$ 14. $9 - 8 = \boxed{1}$ 15. $10 - 4 = \boxed{6}$

Name _____

PATH to FLUENCY

Fluency Check 12

Add.

1. $3 + 3 = \boxed{6}$ 2. $6 + 1 = \boxed{7}$ 3. $4 + 2 = \boxed{6}$

4. $3 + 4 = \boxed{7}$ 5. $6 + 2 = \boxed{8}$ 6. $5 + 4 = \boxed{9}$

Subtract.

7. $6 - 4 = \boxed{2}$ 8. $8 - 5 = \boxed{3}$ 9. $7 - 3 = \boxed{4}$

10. $8 - 6 = \boxed{2}$ 11. $9 - 2 = \boxed{7}$ 12. $7 - 1 = \boxed{6}$

13. $10 - 10 = \boxed{0}$ 14. $10 - 7 = \boxed{3}$ 15. $9 - 8 = \boxed{1}$

PATH to FLUENCY Fluency Check 14

Subtract.

1.
$$\begin{array}{r} 4 \\ -2 \\ \hline 2 \end{array}$$

2.
$$\begin{array}{r} 5 \\ -1 \\ \hline 4 \end{array}$$

3.
$$\begin{array}{r} 3 \\ -3 \\ \hline 0 \end{array}$$

4.
$$\begin{array}{r} 6 \\ -5 \\ \hline 1 \end{array}$$

5.
$$\begin{array}{r} 7 \\ -4 \\ \hline 3 \end{array}$$

6.
$$\begin{array}{r} 6 \\ -3 \\ \hline 3 \end{array}$$

7.
$$\begin{array}{r} 8 \\ -3 \\ \hline 5 \end{array}$$

8.
$$\begin{array}{r} 8 \\ -8 \\ \hline 0 \end{array}$$

9.
$$\begin{array}{r} 7 \\ -2 \\ \hline 5 \end{array}$$

10.
$$\begin{array}{r} 9 \\ -6 \\ \hline 3 \end{array}$$

11.
$$\begin{array}{r} 8 \\ -5 \\ \hline 3 \end{array}$$

12.
$$\begin{array}{r} 9 \\ -4 \\ \hline 5 \end{array}$$

13.
$$\begin{array}{r} 10 \\ -3 \\ \hline 7 \end{array}$$

14.
$$\begin{array}{r} 10 \\ -8 \\ \hline 2 \end{array}$$

15.
$$\begin{array}{r} 9 \\ -3 \\ \hline 6 \end{array}$$

PATH to FLUENCY Fluency Check 13

Add.

1.
$$\begin{array}{r} 1 \\ +2 \\ \hline 3 \end{array}$$

2.
$$\begin{array}{r} 3 \\ +1 \\ \hline 4 \end{array}$$

3.
$$\begin{array}{r} 2 \\ +3 \\ \hline 5 \end{array}$$

4.
$$\begin{array}{r} 2 \\ +4 \\ \hline 6 \end{array}$$

5.
$$\begin{array}{r} 4 \\ +3 \\ \hline 7 \end{array}$$

6.
$$\begin{array}{r} 6 \\ +1 \\ \hline 7 \end{array}$$

7.
$$\begin{array}{r} 4 \\ +4 \\ \hline 8 \end{array}$$

8.
$$\begin{array}{r} 5 \\ +2 \\ \hline 7 \end{array}$$

9.
$$\begin{array}{r} 4 \\ +5 \\ \hline 9 \end{array}$$

10.
$$\begin{array}{r} 6 \\ +3 \\ \hline 9 \end{array}$$

11.
$$\begin{array}{r} 5 \\ +3 \\ \hline 8 \end{array}$$

12.
$$\begin{array}{r} 8 \\ +2 \\ \hline 10 \end{array}$$

13.
$$\begin{array}{r} 6 \\ +2 \\ \hline 8 \end{array}$$

14.
$$\begin{array}{r} 5 \\ +5 \\ \hline 10 \end{array}$$

15.
$$\begin{array}{r} 2 \\ +7 \\ \hline 9 \end{array}$$

PATH to FLUENCY Fluency Check 16

Subtract.

1. $2 - 1 = \boxed{1}$

2. $4 - 2 = \boxed{2}$

3. $3 - 0 = \boxed{3}$

4. $5 - 4 = \boxed{1}$

5. $6 - 3 = \boxed{3}$

6. $7 - 5 = \boxed{2}$

7. $6 - 4 = \boxed{2}$

8. $8 - 8 = \boxed{0}$

9. $7 - 3 = \boxed{4}$

10. $8 - 6 = \boxed{2}$

11. $9 - 2 = \boxed{7}$

12. $9 - 5 = \boxed{4}$

13. $10 - 8 = \boxed{2}$

14. $8 - 3 = \boxed{5}$

15. $10 - 4 = \boxed{6}$

PATH to FLUENCY Fluency Check 15

Add.

1. $1 + 1 = \boxed{2}$

2. $5 + 3 = \boxed{8}$

3. $3 + 1 = \boxed{4}$

4. $5 + 5 = \boxed{10}$

5. $4 + 4 = \boxed{8}$

6. $5 + 1 = \boxed{6}$

7. $4 + 3 = \boxed{7}$

8. $4 + 5 = \boxed{9}$

9. $5 + 2 = \boxed{7}$

Find the unknown partner.

10. $1 + \boxed{7} = 8$

11. $3 + \boxed{3} = 6$

12. $5 + \boxed{3} = 8$

13. $\boxed{6} + 3 = 9$

14. $\boxed{5} + 5 = 10$

15. $\boxed{8} + 2 = 10$

PATH to FLUENCY

Fluency Check 18

Add.

1. $2 + 2 = \boxed{4}$ 2. $3 + 3 = \boxed{6}$ 3. $1 + 3 = \boxed{4}$

4. $3 + 2 = \boxed{5}$ 5. $4 + 3 = \boxed{7}$ 6. $1 + 7 = \boxed{8}$

7. $2 + 4 = \boxed{6}$ 8. $4 + 6 = \boxed{10}$ 9. $6 + 2 = \boxed{8}$

10. $7 + 2 = \boxed{9}$ 11. $5 + 4 = \boxed{9}$ 12. $7 + 3 = \boxed{10}$

13. $\boxed{8} = 3 + 5$ 14. $\boxed{10} = 2 + 8$ 15. $\boxed{9} = 5 + 4$

PATH to FLUENCY

Fluency Check 17

Add.

1. $\begin{array}{r} 0 \\ +1 \\ \hline 1 \end{array}$ 2. $\begin{array}{r} 3 \\ +0 \\ \hline 3 \end{array}$ 3. $\begin{array}{r} 1 \\ +1 \\ \hline 2 \end{array}$

4. $\begin{array}{r} 2 \\ +2 \\ \hline 4 \end{array}$ 5. $\begin{array}{r} 1 \\ +5 \\ \hline 6 \end{array}$ 6. $\begin{array}{r} 3 \\ +4 \\ \hline 7 \end{array}$

7. $\begin{array}{r} 4 \\ +2 \\ \hline 6 \end{array}$ 8. $\begin{array}{r} 8 \\ +0 \\ \hline 8 \end{array}$ 9. $\begin{array}{r} 2 \\ +5 \\ \hline 7 \end{array}$

10. $\begin{array}{r} 6 \\ +1 \\ \hline 7 \end{array}$ 11. $\begin{array}{r} 3 \\ +5 \\ \hline 8 \end{array}$ 12. $\begin{array}{r} 7 \\ +2 \\ \hline 9 \end{array}$

13. $\begin{array}{r} 2 \\ +8 \\ \hline 10 \end{array}$ 14. $\begin{array}{r} 3 \\ +6 \\ \hline 9 \end{array}$ 15. $\begin{array}{r} 6 \\ +4 \\ \hline 10 \end{array}$

Solve the story problem.
Show your work.

5. Nina sees 9 ducks in the pond. 4 ducks are white.
The rest are black.

Complete the subtraction equation and the addition
equation. How many ducks are black?

$9 - \boxed{5} = 4$

$4 + \boxed{5} = 9$

$\boxed{5}$ black ducks

6. Use addition to solve subtraction.

$4 + 2 = 6$, so I know $6 - 2 = \boxed{4}$.

7. Add both sides.
What number makes the equation true?

$4 + \boxed{3} = 5 + 2$

8–9. Find the unknown partner.

$6 + \boxed{4} = 10$

$9 - \boxed{3} = 6$

Operations and Algebraic Thinking

Write the correct answer.

1. Write how many are left.
Use the picture to help you.

There are 6 frogs.

$6 - 4 = \boxed{2}$

Then 4 hop away.

Solve the story problem.
Show your work.

2. Amanda has 8 flower stickers, 2 heart stickers,
and 9 car stickers. How many stickers does
Amanda have in all?

$\boxed{19}$ stickers
label

3. Write the 10-partners
and switch the partners.

$8 + 2$

$2 + 8$

4. Use the 5-group.
Write how many.

$\boxed{7}$

17. Use the grid to find 10 more.

21	22	23	24	25	26	27	28	29	30
31	32	33	34	35	36	37	38	39	40
41	42	43	44	45	46	47	48	49	50

10 more than 32 is 42 .

18–19. Solve.

$50 - 0 = \boxed{50}$ $60 + \boxed{10} = 70$

Number an

10. Start at 61.
Write the missing numbers to

61	62	63	64	65	66	6		78	89	90
71	72	73	74	75	76	77	78			
81	82	83	84	85	86	87	88	89	90	

11. How many jars of paint are there?

26 jars

12–13. Write the number.

8 tens 0 ones = 80   1 ten 7 ones = 17

Measurement and Data

20. Number the cars in order from shortest to longest.

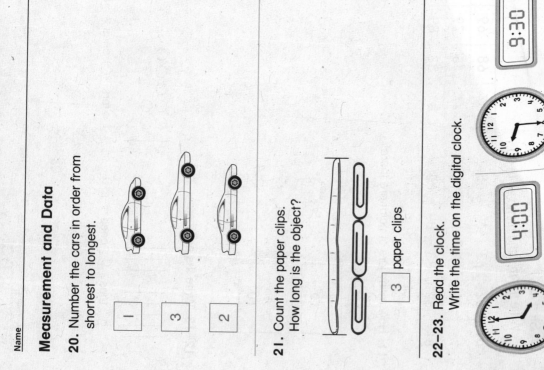

1

3

2

21. Count the paper clips. How long is the object?

3 paper clips

22-23. Read the clock. Write the time on the digital clock.

4:00

9:30

24-25. Use the data to complete.

Our Favorite Flower

Rose	○	○	○	○	○	○	○	○
Tulip	○	○	○	○				
Daisy	○	○	○	○	○	○		

How many children chose the tulip as their favorite flower?

4 children

How many more children chose the rose than the daisy?

2 more children

---

29. Ring the shape used to make the larger shape.

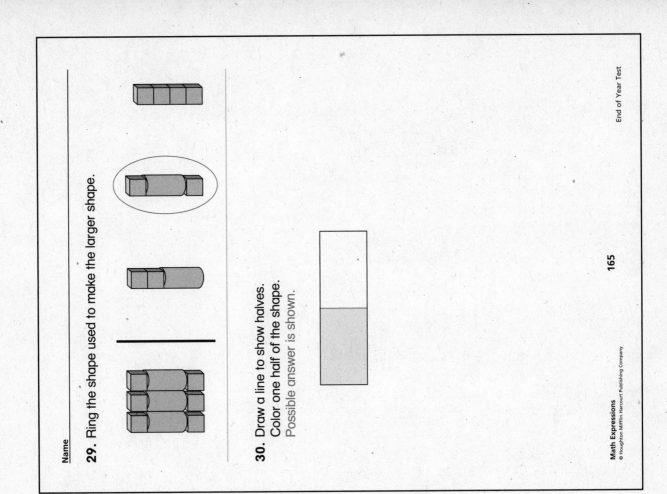

30. Draw a line to show halves.
Color one half of the shape.
Possible answer is shown.

Geometry

26. Which shapes are squares?
Draw an X on each one.

27. Which shapes are NOT circles?
Draw an X on each one.

28. Join these two squares.

Ring the new shape they make.

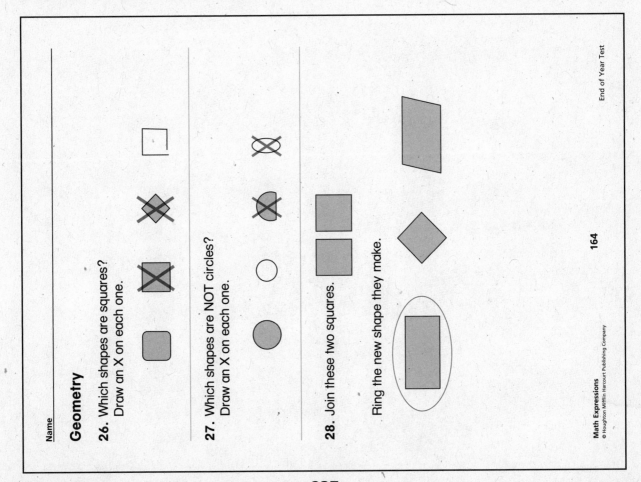